TIME
OF THE
PREACHER

FOR A MOMENT, I JUST STAND STILL AMIDST THE CHAOS, STARING IN DUMB DISBELIEF, OBLIVIOUS OF THE FLASHFIRE OF TERROR THAT RAGES ABOUT ME.

I HEAR SCREAMS, AS THOUGH FROM A GREAT DISTANCE, AND THE SOUNDS OF A TERRIBLE SLAUGHTER.

...BUT NOTHING I SEE IS REAL.

AND THE ONLY BLOOD THAT FLOWS IS MINE.

ONCE MORE, I RUN.

ONLY TO BE BROUGHT DOWN...

...BY THE MANNEQUIN VERSION OF ME.

THE WINDOW SHATTERS.

AND PART OF ME WELCOMES THIS FINAL PLUNGE...

...TO THE GROUND SO FAR BELOW.

WHAT!!? WHERE =?!

A ROOM OF SOME KIND, OLD AND ROTTEN. THE METAL WALLS THICK WITH SLIME AND RUST, THE AIR STALE.

WHOEVER = WHATEVER = MY PURSUER IS, I KNOW NOW IT WON'T STOP UNTIL ONE OF US IS SLAIN.

I HAVE TO HIDE.

OH!!?!

IT'S AS THOUGH THE WINDOW WAS ACTUALLY A WALL, AND THE SKY BEYOND SOME PAINTED ILLUSION LIKE THE BACKDROP OF A STAGE SET.

ABOVE ME, I CAN SEE THE BALLROOM.

I TRIPPED!

OVER MY OWN FEET?!

MADNESS UPON MADNESS.

I START TO WAIL.

I CAN'T ENDURE ANY MORE.

I WANT TO GIVE UP.

BUT SOMETHING INSIDE WON'T LET ME.

IT'S LIKE THE TALES OF CLASSICAL HELL.

EACH CIRCLE OF TORMENT GIVES WAY TO ONE IMMEASURABLY WORSE.

AS LUCIEN DELACROIX'S *SON* AND *HEIR*, I AM OBLIGED TO LOOK AFTER HIS BEST INTERESTS, AND THE FIRM'S.

AS A GOOD SON SHOULD. HOW NOBLE OF YOU, *MEIN HERR*.

I DON'T SEE WHAT'S SO SPECIAL ABOUT HER.

NO *SHARI*, YOU WOULDN'T.

I'M *BETTER* THAN HER, WILLEM. I'M *PERFECT* AND I'M *YOUNG.* THAT'LL NEVER CHANGE.

I'M *YOURS* FOREVER-- WHY CAN'T THAT BE ENOUGH?

IS THERE A CAUSE, DOCTOR?

CARYN'S BENCHMARK TESTS INDICATE AN EXCEPTIONALLY *STABLE* PERSONALITY.

HER LIFE HISTORY BEARS THAT OUT.

SHE HAS BEEN EVALUATED BY MY OWN STAFF, AND THE CORPORATION'S COMPUTER NEXUS, *TOY.*

TO THE BEST OF OUR KNOWLEDGE AND ABILITY-- WHICH IS CONSIDERABLE--

-- WE CAN DETERMINE NEITHER A PHYSICAL NOR A PSYCHOLOGICAL CAUSE FOR THIS CONDITION.

CAN SHE SEE US?

NO. THE CAMERAS ARE HIDDEN.

SHE *ALWAYS* LOOKS TOWARD THE LENS.

AS THOUGH SHE KNOWS PRECISELY WHERE IT IS.

IS THAT YOUR FINAL JUDGMENT, DR. JOHANNES?

IT IS MY *FORMAL* JUDGMENT, HERR DELACROIX.

AND SO I SHALL REPORT TO YOUR *FATHER.*

...THIS IS NOT APPROPRIATE.

I'M ALREADY PLEDGED. I WON'T BETRAY THAT TRUST.

CARYN, WHAT ARE YOU THINKING? I WOULD NEVER *DREAM*--!

FORGIVE ME, IF I GAVE THE WRONG IMPRESSION. CONSIDER IT A CASE OF YOUTHFUL EXUBERANCE.

I WAS DAZZLED BY YOUR BEAUTY-- AS ANY MAN WOULD BE.

BUT ALL I WANT IS TO BE YOUR TRUE FRIEND.

THANK YOU. IT'S WHAT I NEED MOST THESE DAYS.

CAN I ESCORT YOU HOME? TO MAKE AMENDS FOR PUTTING YOU SO ILL AT EASE?

WILLEM, WHAT ABOUT *SHARI?*

WHAT ABOUT HER?

KLIK
KLAK
KLIK
KLAK
KLIK
KLAK
KLIK

DAMN THE GIRL!

MITCHELL!

GO AFTER HER, MAKE SURE SHE'S ALL RIGHT.

HELP HER BUY SOMETHING NICE, THAT'LL MAKE HER FEEL BETTER.

RIGHT AWAY, MR. DELACROIX.

YOU HURT HER.

SHE'S A *TROPHY.* SHE CAN'T BE HURT.

I'M A TROPHY, TOO, WILLEM.

WHO KNOWS? PERHAPS WHAT-EVER'S WRONG WITH ME IS CATCHING.

CLEAR AWAY! *CLEAR AWAY!*

HEY! SHARI!!! *WAIT UP!!!*

WATCH IT--!

WH*OW!*

YOU DUMB *BABOOTCH*--

-- COUNT YOURSELF LUCKY YOU'RE MOVIN' SO DAMN FAST!

YO, MARIA-- *CHILL!*

THE HELL YOU SAY, TOMMY--I WANT HIS *ASS!*

'BEHAVE *DOMEDICI.* I MEAN IT! WE'RE *WAY* OFF OUR TURF HERE!'

I CAN'T LEAVE YOU ALONE, MISS, I GOT MY ORDERS.

IT ISN'T FAIR, MITCHELL.

BE REAL, SHARI, I'M A BODYGUARD, YOU'RE A TROPHY ESCORT. WE DO WHAT WE'RE TOLD AN' THERE'S THE END OF IT.

LIFESTYLES OF THE RULING CLASS AIN'T THEY SWEET!

WILL YOU STOP TENSING, TOMMY, EVERY TIME I OPEN MY MOUTH--JEEZ, YOU'RE GIVIN' ME A COMPLEX, Y'HEAR WHAT I'M SAYIN'?

YOU'RE GIVING ME A DAMN ULCER!

WELL, EXCUSE ME ALL TA HELL!

SINCE WHEN YOU EVER GET THE HEEBIE-JEEBIES SIMPLY 'CAUSE WE DECIDE T'BREAK A FEW RULES?

LAWS, MARIA, NOT RULES. WE'RE COMMITTING A MAJOR-LEAGUE *FELONY* JUST BY BEING HERE.

ONLY IF THEY CATCH US.

I OUGHT TO HAVE MY SKULL POPPED FOR LETTING YOU TALK ME INTO THIS.

I'M NOT SPOOKIN', TOMAS.

I TAGGED A HARD, LEGIT CONTACT--VERY SMALL, VERY FAST-- SLIPPING DOWN OFF THE PLANE OF THE ECLIPTIC DURING A SOLAR STORM THAT SCRAMBLED SCANNERS ALL ACROSS THE SYSTEM.

COINCIDENCE. STORM GHOST. EQUIPMENT MALFUNCTION. OPERATOR ERROR.

MY HARDWARE DON'T MAKE MISTAKES, AN' NEITHER DO I.

I'VE CROSSLINKED MY REPORT TO YOUR BUFFER, SEIGNEUR.

BUT I MUST ASK, WOULD YOU NOT PERHAPS BE BETTER SERVED BY A MORE... STABLE COMPANION?

I SENT MY WIFE TO YOU, DR. JOHANNES, BECAUSE YOU ASSURED ME YOU COULD BE OF HELP TO HER.

THIS SUGGESTION IS NOT HELPFUL.

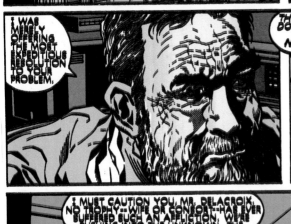

I WAS MERELY OFFERING THE MOST EXPEDITIOUS RESOLUTION TO YOUR PROBLEM.

THE "PROBLEM," DOCTOR, IS THAT MY WIFE HAS NIGHTMARES.

I DO NOT WISH TO LOSE CARYN, OR DISPOSE OF HER.

I WANT THE NIGHTMARES TO STOP.

I MUST CAUTION YOU, MR. DELACROIX. NO TROPHY -- WIFE OR CONSORT -- HAS EVER SUFFERED SUCH AN AFFLICTION. WE'RE PUSHING INTO THE UNKNOWN. THE COURSE OF TREATMENT YOU MANDATE MAY HAVE AWKWARD RAMIFICATIONS.

I WANT CARYN HAPPY, DOCTOR. I WANT HER BACK THE WAY SHE WAS. ANYTHING LESS IS UNACCEPTABLE.

KEEP ME INFORMED OF YOUR PROGRESS. AND DON'T MAKE ME WAIT.

OH, CARYN, CARYN CARYN...

WHAT A CONUNDRUM YOU ARE.

WHAT A MESS THIS IS.

HE WANTS YOU HAPPY AND HE WANTS YOU BY HIS SIDE.

SUPPOSE THE TWO ARE MUTUALLY EXCLUSIVE?

ASH!!! PALNALL?

GASP!

MATER CHRISTI...

NO!

WELCOME TO *STRUCTURES*, CARYN. HOW MAY WE BE OF SERVICE, TODAY?

I'M TIRED OF THE WAY I LOOK, TOY.

I'D LIKE TO BECOME SOMEONE COMPLETELY *DIFFERENT*.

ALAS, MADAME, WE CAN ONLY ACCOMPLISH THAT IN A PURELY *PHYSICAL* SENSE.

ANYTHING MORE WILL HAVE TO BE UP TO YOU.

HAVE YOU ANYTHING SPECIFIC IN MIND OR WOULD YOU PREFER TO SEE A SELECTION?

I WISH I KNEW.

SELECTION, THEN. IS MADAME CONSIDERING A CHANGE IN GENDER?

GOOD GRACIOUS, NO! IN THAT REGARD, I'LL STAY AS I AM.

WELCOME TO STRUCTURES, SIR... HOW MAY WE BE OF SERVICE?

MAKE ME LOOK LIKE CARYN, TOY. I WANT TO BE HER TWIN, IDENTICAL IN EVERY WAY!

IF I LOOK LIKE HER, IF I GIVE WILLEM THE OBJECT OF HIS *DESIRE*...

ALL I WANT IS FOR HIM TO LOVE ME... THE WAY I DO HIM.

DUPLICATE PHYSIOG-NOMIES ARE NORMALLY PROHIBITED, SIR... HOWEVER, SINCE CARYN IS ALTERING HER OWN APPEARANCE, YOUR REQUEST HAS BEEN APPROVED.

IS THAT SO WRONG?

A PRIVATE VIEWING CUBICLE... HAS BEEN PREPARED FOR YOU, CARYN. THIS WAY.

THANK YOU, TOY.

TELL ME, AM I DOING THE RIGHT THING?

IT IS WHAT YOU ASKED FOR, CARYN.

FINE, I GOT THE NUMBER WRONG.

GO BACK TO 300, TAKE US *SLOWLY* UP FROM THERE. IF THAT DOESN'T WORK, START FROM THE BEGINNING.

I *WANT* THAT FACE!

CARYN, WE HAVE NOW RUN THE ENTIRE INVENTORY, TWICE.

I DON'T UNDER-STAND.

I KNOW WHAT I SAW.

IT'S GOT TO BE HERE!

NOT NECESSARILY. IT COULD HAVE BEEN SOME ELEMENT OF IMAGINATION, OR MEMORY, TRANS-POSED OVER THE VIEWING CYCLE.

THIS IS THE STRUCTURE YOU RESPONDED TO. IT FULFILLS YOUR STATED PARAMETERS. IT IS QUITE BECOMING.

HOWEVER, IF YOU CAN PROVIDE A DESCRIPTION, I CAN ATTEMPT TO REPLI-CATE THIS OTHER FORM YOU REFER TO.

I ONLY GOT A GLIMPSE, I CAN'T REMEMBER!

WHAT'S HAPPENING TO ME, TOY?! WHY DO I KEEP SEEING THAT FACE?! WHY DOES IT MAKE ME SO *AFRAID?*

GIVEN THE STATED PARAMETERS, I AM UNABLE TO ANSWER YOUR QUESTION AT THIS TIME.

UNDER THE CIRCUMSTANCES, HOWEVER...

...I PERCEIVE NO RATIONAL JUSTI-FICATION FOR YOUR APPREHENSION.

I'M *IRRATIONAL*, THEN!

THERE IS NO REASON.

NOR ANY TO BE AFRAID.

BUT MY *NIGHT-MARES*, TOY!

THIS SENSE THAT SOME-THING'S *HUNTING* ME!

GIVEN TIME, CARYN, I HAVE NO DOUBT THAT A PERFECTLY LOGICAL EXPLANATION WILL PRESENT ITSELF.

FOR NOW, HOW-EVER, YOU ARE IN THE *SAFEST* OF HANDS.

AS YOU CAST OFF THIS OLD SKIN, CAST OFF ITS CARES AS WELL.

TRUST ME, CARYN.

WITH MY *LIFE*, TOY.

JUST LIKE ALWAYS.

I SHOULDN'T FEEL LIKE THIS.

TROPHIES CHANGE THEIR SKIN ALMOST AS OFTEN AS THEIR CLOTHES. OUR GENETICALLY ENGINEERED *MUTABILITY* IS ONE OF OUR "SELLING" POINTS.

BUT THOUGH IT'S A CUSTOM DESIGN, MY NEW BODY JUST WON'T FIT.

MITCHELL! WHY'S IT SO COLD?

I FEEL AS OUT OF PLACE AS SHARI LOOKS, WEARING MY OLD LIKENESS.

I WONDER HOW MUCH IT HAS TO DO WITH THAT STRANGE MATRIX I KEEP SEEING. SUCH AN ORDINARY WOMAN, NOTHING SPECTACULAR AT ALL; HER FACE IS LINED.

SHARI'S WHINE DOESN'T REGISTER AT FIRST. I HADN'T NOTICED THE CHILL, I NEVER DO.

BUT THAT ISN'T ALL.

MITCHELL, THE *WINDOW--!*

A SCARLET LIGHT FLASHES FROM DEEP WITHIN THE FOG. I FEEL FAINT PINPRICKS OF HEAT ON MY FOREHEAD.

TARGETING LASER!

CARYN-- SHARI-- *GET DOWN!*

MITCHELL'S VERY GOOD-- MONTCALM-DELACROIX ONLY EMPLOYS THE *BEST*-- WITH BIONIC ENHANCEMENTS SPECIFIC TO THE TRADE OF *BODYGUARD.*

HE HAS HIS GUN OUT ALMOST FASTER THAN THE EYE CAN FOLLOW.

BUT HE'S STILL ONLY *HUMAN*.

ZAP!

AS THE SIGHTING TREFOIL LOCKS ONTO MITCHELL...

...I FIND MYSELF REACTING TO SAVE HIM.

THE DECK CHAIR'S THE ONLY WEAPON AT HAND.

TO MY AMAZEMENT, I HIT SOMETHING.

IT ISN'T *AMUSED*.

MITCHELL GOES AFTER IT, WITH A VENGEANCE.

I'VE SEEN HIM FIGHT-- AND FLATTEN-- MEN TWICE HIS SIZE WITH A SINGLE PUNCH.

NOT THIS TIME.

BY *DAMN*, WHAT ARE YOU TWO DOING HERE STILL?!

THIS IS A *KILLING GROUND*, WOMAN! GET OUT OF HERE *NOW*!

I'LL HOLD THIS BASTARD, BEST I CAN! *GO!*

REMEMBER: Ship SECURITY OFFICERS are your FRIENDS.

They are here to SERVE and PROTECT.

It is a citizen's duty to COOPERATE at all times, under penalty of LAW.

FREEZE!

WHAT THE HELL?!

NOBODY MOVES, NOBODY DIES!

FUNNY, I DON' REMEMBER CALLIN' ROOM SERVICE.

RISE AND SHINE, LOVEBIRDS -- YOU'RE COMIN' WITH US.

AS WE ARE?

HEY, SKELL, WORKS FOR ME.

NICE OF 'EM TO LET US GET DRESSED, TOMMY. I GUESS THEY'RE REAL GENTLEMEN AFTER ALL.

IF YOU DON'T MIND THE FACT THAT THEY WATCHED OUR EVERY MOVE.

THE SKANK WHO HIT YOU, BET THAT WAS LOVE AT FIRST SIGHT, Y'KNOW?

SHUT YOUR TRAP, HONEY, OR YOU'LL GET THE SAME.

PROMISES, PROMISES.

RUMBLES ARE SERIOUSLY AGITATED.

NOTICED THAT, DID YOU?

I'M VERY PERCEPTIVE. THIS WHOLE SECTION'S UNDER A STAGE RED ALERT. THEY'RE SPOOKED SO BAD...

...YOU'D THINK THEY JUST HATCHED A QUEEN EMBRYO.

TOLD YOU THAT'D BE TROUBLE, TOMMY.

NOBODY EVER LISTENS TO ME.

IT WAS IN THE VICINITY OF THE OFFICE OF DR. ERIK JOHANNES.

WE HAD NOTHING DEFINITE. A GHOST CONTACT AT BEST.

YOUR "*GHOST*" HAS SLAUGHTERED THREE PEOPLE. WE FOUND JOHANNES, LOOKING MUCH LIKE THIS!

WANNA KNOW WHAT I'M THINKIN', TOMMY?

THIS COULD'A BEEN US.

ABSOLUTELY.

DAMN YOU BOTH, I WANT *ANSWERS!*

ALL WE KNOW, WE PUT IN THE SIGHTING REPORT.

ASN'T "BUG" AT DID T, WE'LL T YOU R EE.

WE'RE NOT SECURITY, *SEIGNEUR.* THERE'S NOTHING WE CAN OFFER HERE.

YOU DON'T UNDERSTAND. THERE WERE *THREE* PEOPLE ON THIS DECK.

TWO WERE MURDERED. BUT THE THIRD-- MY FATHER'S TROPHY WIFE-- HAS *VANISHED.*

WITHOUT A TRACE.

TOO BAD, SHE'D'A BEEN LUCKIER TO END UP LIKE THIS.

THE HEAT MAKES ME THINK OF HELL.

EXCEPT I KNOW THAT I'M NOT DEAD.

YET.

WORSE BY FAR, I KNOW AT LAST THIS IS NO DREAM.

I THINK OF SHARI AND MITCHELL...

...AND CAN'T HELP WONDERING...

ASH...

IN MY WHOLE LIFE, I'VE NEVER WALKED ON THE GROUND.

THE ALIENS LIVED ON THE GROUND. EVEN THOUGH THEY'VE BEEN DRIVEN FROM THE EARTH, THE OLD FEARS REMAIN. THAT'S WHY WE LIVE IN THE SKY, WHERE IT'S SAFE.

THIS CREATURE DOESN'T SEEM TO CARE.

IT'S SO HOT, I CAN'T HELP THINKING OF HELL.

AND WONDERING IF I'M FACE TO FACE WITH THE DEVIL.

ASH, PARNALL...!

THAT'S ALL IT SAYS TO ME.

IT ISN'T HAPPY THAT I DON'T KNOW THE PROPER REPLY.

I WANT TO GO HOME.

I DON'T WANT TO DIE.

THERE'S BLOOD ON MY GOWN, ON MY FACE. IT ISN'T MINE. NOT YET.

MITCHELL TRIED TO PROTECT SHARI AND ME. HE FOUGHT AS HARD AS HE COULD. THE CREATURE TOOK HIS SKULL AS A TROPHY.

AND AS FOR SHARI...

ELSEWHERE... FOR THE RECORD, THIS IS THE SKYLINER *LIBERTÉ*...

...REGISTERED TERRESTRIAL CORPORATE HEAD-QUARTERS OF *MONTCALM-DELACROIX et CIE.*

PRESIDING CORPORATE OFFICER AT THIS *INTERROGATION* IS *WILLEM DELACROIX,* JUNIOR MEMBER OF THE BOARD.

PRESIDING *INVESTIGATOR* IS CORPORATE CHIEF OF SECURITY, *GISANDE SALAZAR.*

AGAIN, FOR THE RECORD, IF YOU WOULD PLEASE IDENTIFY YOURSELVES...

TOMAS SHIROW.

MARIA DeMEDICI.

THIS INTERRO-GATION IS PART OF AN ONGOING INQUIRY INTO THE DEATHS BY VIOLENCE EARLIER THIS EVENING OF EXECUTIVE BODYGUARD *MITCHELL LASSITER* AND EXECUTIVE COMPANION *SHARI.*

WASN'T US, CHIEF.

YOUR INVOLVEMENT-- AND THE CONSEQUENCES THEREOF-- REMAIN TO BE DETERMINED.

LEMME GUESS-- DEPENDING ON THE DEGREE OF OUR COOPERATION, AM I RIGHT?

IN ADDITION, *CARYN DELACROIX*-- WIFE OF CHIEF EXECUTIVE *LUCIEN DELACROIX*-- HAS DISAPPEARED. WE BELIEVE SHE MAY HAVE BEEN ABDUCTED BY WHOEVER COMMITTED THESE MURDERS.

THIS SURVEILLANCE VIDEO WAS TAKEN ON THE PROMENADE DECK.

I TOOK THE LIBERTY OF HAVING *TOY* EXECUTE A FULL-SPECTRUM REFERENCE SCAN ON THE PAIR OF YOU.

I TOLD YOU SO. BUT *YOU* SAID THEY'D NEVER BOTHER.

NOBODY *EVER* LISTENS TO ME. WHY IS THAT?

WHO'S *"TOY"*?

SOME MIGHT CALL HIM A *WHAT*, ACTUALLY. BUT WE'VE KNOWN EACH OTHER, AND WORKED TOGETHER, FOR SO LONG, I'VE COME TO THINK OF HIM AS A PERSON IN HIS OWN RIGHT.

TOY IS A VERY SPECIAL AND ALTOGETHER UNIQUE COMPUTER SYSTEM.

SALUTATIONS, MAJOR SHIROW, COLONEL DeMEDICI.

FORGIVE THE DELAY, LUCIEN. THE DATA WERE ENCRYPTED ON A RESTRICTED-ACCESS FILE IN THE DEFENSE FORCES MAIN REFERENCE CACHE.

IT WAS NECESSARY TO PERSUADE THE MILITARY OPERATING SYSTEM TO RELEASE IT TO ME.

SO MUCH FOR GUARANTEES OF PRIVACY.

HEY, TOMMY, *ANY* NETWORK CAN BE COMPROMISED.

ESPECIALLY BY THIS *CHARMING* A SYSTEM.

MY THANKS FOR THE COMPLIMENT.

THOMAS SHIROW AND MARIA DeMEDICI ARE *STRIKE FORCE RANGERS*, SPECIALIZING IN LONG-RANGE COMMANDO OPERATIONS. AS *ULTIMATE HAZARD* PERSONNEL, THEY ARE BANNED BY LAW FROM BOARDING ANY CORPORATE SKYLINER.

YOUR CURRENT PRESENCE ON EARTH IS UNAUTHORIZED.

IT'S A CHARACTER FLAW, Y'KNOW? THE MORE WE'RE TOLD TO STEER CLEAR OF SOME-WHERE...

...THE MORE DETERMINED WE ARE TO GO.

IF THIS MATTER WERE TO BE PURSUED, IT IS DOUBTFUL EVEN YOUR MOST FORMID-ABLE RECORDS WOULD SAVE YOU.

AT THE VERY LEAST, YOU WOULD BE CASHIERED IN DISGRACE AND BANISHED UNDER IRREVOCABLE QUARAN-TINE TO SOME REMOTE FRINGE *WORLD*.

ON THE OTHER HAND, WERE YOU TO ASSIST WHOLE-HEARTEDLY IN THE RESOLU-TION OF THIS MATTER...

AM I SUR-PRISED, OR WHAT?

NO GUARANTEES.

ALL I ASK IS THAT YOU TRY.

CONSIDERING THE ALTERNATIVES...

BUT I HAVE TO TELL YOU, *SEIGNEUR*, THE ODDS ARE, YOUR LADY'S ALREADY DEAD.

I WALK FOR MOST OF THE NIGHT...

THE JUNGLE'S VERY QUIET, MORE SO THAN EVER I IMAGINED.

EVERY LIVING THING SCARED AWAY, NO DOUBT, BY THE NEW PREDATOR IN THE NEIGHBORHOOD.

...AND THEN TUCK MYSELF INTO THE BOLE OF A TREE TO WAIT FOR DAWN.

MY MAIN WEAPON IS A COLONIAL MARINE-ISSUE PULSE RIFLE.

FULL CLIP OF TEN-MIL AMMO, PLUS SPARES.

PLUS GRENADES.

BLACK-MARKET PURCHASE, BUT IN FAIR CONDITION. I MAKE IT BETTER.

AND THEN I SIT BACK AND WONDER... HOW?

I'VE JUST FIELD-STRIPPED AND CLEANED A MILITARY RIFLE AS THOUGH I'VE BEEN DOING IT MY WHOLE LIFE.

THIS IS NUTS.

OR I AM.

UNLESS...

I GIGGLE, I CAN'T HELP MYSELF.

THE ANSWER'S SO OBVIOUS, SO ABSURD, IT HAS TO BE TRUE.

IT'S A VIRTUAL REALITY SCENARIO, COMPLETE WITH TEMPORARY KNOWLEDGE IMPLANTS-- SOMETHING LUCIEN HAD TOY WHIP UP, I'LL BET, TO TAKE MY MIND OFF MY TROUBLES.

A LITTLE MORE ROUGH-TRADE THAN I'M USED TO, BUT PERHAPS DR. JOHANNES FELT I NEEDED THE CATHARSIS.

...BUT I'M TOO RELIEVED TO DISCOVER THIS IS ONLY A GAME.

NOW I CAN ENJOY MYSELF.

NONE OF THIS IS REAL.

I SHOULD BE ANGRY...

THAT'S THE BEAUTY OF VIRTUAL.

GO ANYWHERE, DO ANYTHING TOY'S IMAGINATION CAN CONCEIVE.

AND NEVER HAVE TO WORRY ABOUT THE OUTCOME.

WIN OR LOSE, YOU'LL NEVER GET HURT.

WHZZZZZ

STUPID STUPID **STUPID!**

SHOULD HAVE BEEN PAYING ATTENTION.

FORGOT THE DAMN SCENARIO.

CREATURE FOUND ME, SOMEHOW CUT MY LINE.

I GRAB ANOTHER.

LET THE MOMENTUM OF MY FALL START ME SPINNING.

AND PULL THE TRIGGER.

BRRPP

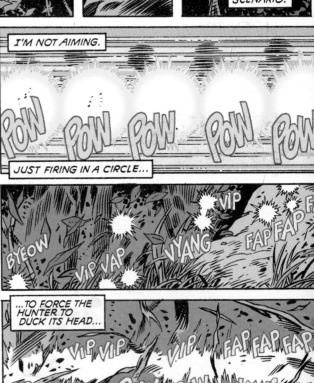

I'M NOT AIMING.

POW POW POW POW POW

JUST FIRING IN A CIRCLE...

BYEOW VIP VAP VIP VYANG FAP FAP F

...TO FORCE THE HUNTER TO DUCK ITS HEAD...

VIP VIP VIP FAP FAP FAP

POW BYEOW POW POW VYANG POW

...AND
IT DOW

THE GUN'S VERY IMPRESSIVE-- TWO HUNDRED ROUNDS GONE IN A MATTER OF SECONDS.

PITY I DIDN'T HIT ANY- THING BUT JUNGLE--

--BUT THEN I ASSUME TOY DIDN'T WANT TO MAKE THIS SCENARIO *TOO* EASY FOR ME.

I'M RUNNING THE MOMENT I HIT THE GROUND.

RELOADING MY RIFLE WITHIN THE FIRST HALF-DOZEN STEPS.

IT'S RUGGED, HIGHLAND COUNTRY.

I USE THAT TO BEST ADVANTAGE.

UPSLOPE, TO MAKE MY PURSUER CLIMB AFTER ME AND SLOW IT DOWN.

OPEN LAND, TO DENY IT COVER.

I RUN A RANDOM, ZIGZAG PATTERN...

...TO DENY IT A CLEAR SHOT FOR ITS LASER.

ALL THE RIGHT IDEAS.

BUT MY BODY ISN'T UP TO FUL- FILLING THEM.

I'M **PERFECT** FOR SOME THINGS. NOT THIS.

I CATCH A SENSE OF MOVEMENT IN THE TREES.

A SHIMMER WHERE THERE SHOULD BE STILLNESS.

LIKE HEAT HAZE RIPPLING THE AIR.

MY BODY REACTS OF ITS OWN ACCORD.

GRENADES, THIS TIME, A RAPID- FIRE SPREAD.

PUM PUM PUM

IF IT'S USING THE TREES...

...LET'S SEE WHAT HAPPENS WHEN I KNOCK THEM DOWN.

GREAT CONCEPT.

NOT SO GREAT EXECUTION...

...AS ONE TRUNK TOPPLES ANOTHER IN A CASCADING CHAIN REACTION...

...THAT HEADS RIGHT FOR ME!

NO TIME TO BE ARTFUL.

I SIMPLY PUT MY HEAD DOWN AND RUN FOR MY LIFE.

WHICH ONLY MAKES THINGS WORSE...

...AS I TAKE A TUMBLE OFF THE TRAIL...

YYII!

...AND DOWN A SLOPE SO STEEP IT'S ALMOST VERTICAL!

Oh SHIT!

I SEE ROCKS.

I HIT WATER.

ROCKS WOULD'VE BEEN BETTER.

ARRRGH!

THAT'S THE LAST I KNOW...

...UNTIL I FIND MYSELF PADDLING WEAKLY TOWARDS THE WATERFALL.

THE CURRENT'S SWIFTER BENEATH THE CATARACT. THE JELLYFISH CAN'T HOLD ON

ALL THE WHILE...

...I'M WAITING FOR MY NEMESIS TO FOLLOW MY SCREAM...

...AND FINISH ME OFF.

NEVER IMAGINED I WASN'T THE ONLY ONE WHO GOT HURT.

GRRAWR!

I HEAR IT ANNOUNCE ITS COMING.

NOT THAT I CAN DO ANYTHING ABOUT IT.

AT FIRST, THE JELLYFISH STINGS WERE SO AWFUL, MY MIND REFUSED TO ACCEPT THE PAIN, AND SHUT DOWN.

NOT ANYMORE.

THAT'S WHEN I SEE IT...

...ATOP THE BLUFF WHERE I FELL...

...OFFERING ITSELF AS A PERFECT TARGET, ARROGANTLY CERTAIN IT CAN KILL ME FIRST.

I WISH I COULD TRY.

BUT NOW THAT THE INITIAL SHOCK OF THE JELLYFISH VENOM'S WEARING OFF, I HURT SO BADLY I CAN BARELY BREATHE.

I COULDN'T MAKE A SOUND-- OR A MOVE-- IF I WANTED TO. I'M AMAZED MY HEART'S STILL BEATING.

WHY'S IT STILL LOOKING?

I'M IN PLAIN SIGHT!

IT'S GOING AWAY!

IS IT PLAYING WITH ME? DRAWING THIS OUT FOR FUN?!

PERHAPS-- BUT THAT DOESN'T FEEL RIGHT.

BLIND, THEN?

IT SAW ME WELL ENOUGH IN THE DARK, AND FOLLOWED MY TRAIL PRETTY DARN EASILY.

ASSUME IT CAN SEE.

BUT MAYBE NOT THE WAY WE DO.

IF THE CREATURE TRACKS HEAT EMANATIONS, MY BODY'S GROWN SO COLD LYING HERE...

...IT MUST BE FAIRLY INDISTINGUISHABLE FROM THE BACKGROUND ROCKS.

ASSUME THAT'S TRUE...

...WHERE DO I GO FROM HERE?

THE MOMENT I STEP OUT FROM BEHIND THE WATERFALL, I'M A TARGET AGAIN.

COULD I CLIMB, THEN...?

THERE ARE CLIMBING WALLS ON THE LINER.

ALL THE THRILL OF MOUNTAINEERING WITHOUT THE ATTENDANT RISKS.

THE RIGHT HOLOGRAM PROJECTION EVEN PROVIDES A SPECTACULAR VIEW.

I'VE TRIED MY SHARE OF THOSE SCENARIOS.

THIS PUTS THEM TO SHAME.

EVERY TIME I CONSIDER QUITTING, I THINK OF MY HUNTER--NO, THE WORD FOR IT, THE ONLY WORD, IS PREDATOR-- AND I PUSH THAT MUCH HARDER.

I WANT ITS HEAD ON A PIKE.

I'VE NEVER FELT SUCH EMOTIONS BEFORE. THEY SCARE ME--

--IN NO SMALL MEASURE BECAUSE THEY FEEL SO GOOD.

NOT SO, MY BODY. IN FAIRLY SHORT ORDER, I COLLECT A WHOLE NEW CATALOG OF MISERIES TO REPLACE THE OLL

BUT I COPE. I ENDURE.

PART OF THE VIRTUAL GAME, I ASSUME. I CAN SUFFER, I CAN BE HURT, BUT NOTHING'S SUPPOSED TO LAST.

ASH!

A WOMAN'S VOICE.

ASH PARNALL!

FROM ABOVE.

AS ACHINGLY FAMILIAR AS THE FACE REFLECTED IN THE WATER BEFORE ME: THIS OTHER FACE THAT HAUNTS MY NIGHTMARES.

THE IMPULSE TO REPLY IS AUTOMATIC.

BUT BEFORE I CAN SPEAK, THE VOICE CHANGES.

ANOTHER WOMAN-- SHARI-- CALLING THE SAME NAME.

ASH PARNALL!

AND I VERY CAREFULLY SNEAK A PEEK...

... AS I HEAR DR. JOHANNES...

CARYN... DELACROIX!

IT'S A MIMIC!

AS WELL AS A CHAMELEON... MATER CHRISTI, IS THERE ANYTHING THAT HORROR CAN'T DO?

BUT WHY ONLY SCRAP WORDS? CAN'T IT CONSTRUCT COMPLETE SENTENCES? HOW MUCH DOES IT ACTUALLY COMPREHEND OF WHAT IT SAYS?

WHO CARES? IT'S ONLY A VIRTUAL SIMULACRUM. IF THOSE ARE ITS LIMITS, THOSE ARE ITS LIMITS.

I TAKE MY TIME BEFORE I MOVE AGAIN.

WHEN I RISK ANOTHER GLIMPSE...

WAY TOO EASY.

HOWEVER IT SPEAKS, IT THINKS. LIKE A HUNTER. IT KNEW I WENT IN THE POOL, AND WHEN IT COULDN'T FIND ME ANYWHERE ELSE...

... IT DETERMINED THE ONLY LOGICAL ALTERNATIVE.

CAN'T GO UP, CAN'T GO DOWN-- I'LL BE A CLEAR TARGET EITHER WAY.

CAN I SCOOT SIDEWAYS ALONG THIS LEDGE?

WHAT'S THIS?

SOME SORT OF OPENING IN THE ROCK--

--MERCIFUL HEAVEN, IT'S A CAVE!

I SEE MOONLIGHT INSIDE. IF THAT MEANS AN OPENING TO THE SURFACE...

... I MIGHT BE ABLE TO CATCH THAT UGLY BASTARD FROM BEHIND! THEN WE'LL SEE WHICH OF US IS THE REAL PREDATOR!

MY ELATION LASTS UNTIL I'M WELL AND TRULY *INSIDE*. UNTIL I REALIZE THAT *TOY*-- DAMN HIS ELECTRONIC SOUL -- HAS KICKED THE GAME UP ANOTHER LEVEL.

THE FLOOR-- WALLS-- COVERED WITH *RESIN!*

AN *ALIEN NEST!*

MY FIRST THOUGHT IS THAT IT'S SUPPOSED TO BE A RELIC OF THE *CONQUEST*, WHEN THOSE MONSTERS OVERRAN THE EARTH.

BUT THE GOOP IS *FRESH*, THE STRUCTURES NEWLY FORMED.

LEFTOVER IT MAY BE...

...BUT ALSO *INHABITED!*

I'M ALREADY ON MY WAY OUT-- EVEN THE JELLYFISH ARE PREFERABLE TO THIS--

-- WHEN I HEAR A GROAN.

SOCORRO, POR FAVOR!

‹FOR THE LOVE OF GOD, PLEASE *HELP ME!*›

‹NOT TO WORRY, BOY-- NOBODY *DIES* WHILE I'M AROUND TO SAVE THEM!›

‹CLOSE YOUR EYES, THIS IS GOING TO MAKE A LITTLE *MESS.*›

KRAKOW

‹I'M CARYN.›

‹ANTONIO.›

‹PLEASED TO MEET YOU, ANTONIO. HOW LONG'VE YOU BEEN HERE?›

‹IT'S BEEN A DAY, SEÑORITA CARYN, SINCE THEY TOOK ME FROM MY HOME!›

THE **ALIENS** CAME WHEN EVERYONE WAS ASLEEP. HE DIDN'T SEE WHAT HAPPENED TO HIS PARENTS, WHICH IS PROBABLY FOR THE BEST.

I DON'T ASK ABOUT THE "FACEHUGGER." I ONLY PRAY WE REACH A QUARANTINE STATION IN TIME.

OUR ADVANTAGE IS THAT, SINCE BUGS PREFER TO HUNT BY NIGHT, THE NEST IS PROBABLY EMPTY.

IF WE CAN GET WELL CLEAR BY MORNING, WE SHOULD BE ALL RIGHT. THEY WON'T RISK BEING SPOTTED IN THE DAYLIGHT.

UNFORTUNATELY, THE CLIMB PROVES A LOT HARDER, AND THE DAWN COMES FAR FASTER THAN I COUNTED ON.

‹ ONCE WE REACH THE TOP, ANTONIO, YOU'VE GOT TO GO AS QUICKLY AS YOU CAN, UNDERSTAND ME? ›

‹ I WILL TRY, CARYN. ›

‹ BUT IT IS SO HARD... TO CATCH MY BREATH. ›

THAT'S WHAT HAPPENS WHEN THE EMBRYO GROWS WITHIN THE CHEST CAVITY.

DAMN IT, **NO!** I'LL **WIN** THIS YET! I'LL FIND A WAY TO **SAVE** YOU!

SAVE... YOU?

FANCY MEETING YOU HERE.

ASH...?

CARYN...?

I KNOW WHICH ANSWER IT WANTS...

... BUT NOT WHICH ONE WILL SAVE ME.

AND THEN, IT DOESN'T MATTER ANYMORE...

OH MY GOD!

AS FAR BACK AS I CAN REMEMBER, THE **ALIENS** HAVE BEEN THE ULTIMATE **BOGEYMEN**.

AS FEROCIOUS IN BEHAVIOR AS THEY ARE HIDEOUS IN APPEARANCE.

THEY'RE BORN **KILLING MACHINES**, AS SUPERBLY OUTFITTED BY NATURE FOR THEIR TASK AS SHARKS. AND JUST AS ELEMENTAL, JUST AS UNKNOWABLE. IF THEY HAVE SENTIENCE, IT'S OF A KIND WE'LL **NEVER** COMPREHEND.

FAST AS THEY ARE, THOUGH, MY PREDATOR IS FASTER.

AND, IMPOSSIBLE AS IT SEEMS...

...EVEN MORE DEADLY.

THE PREDATOR FIGHTS LIKE A CREATURE *POSSESSED*, USING ITS WEAPONS WITH LETHAL ABANDON AND A SKILL THAT HAS TO BE SEEN TO BE BELIEVED.

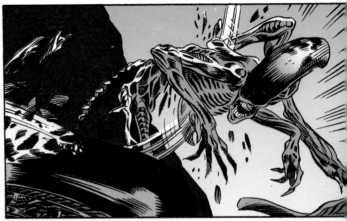

I KEEP IT AT MY BACK...

...SENSING SOMEHOW THAT IT'LL LEAVE ME BE SO LONG AS IT HAS ITS ANCIENT *FOES* TO FIGHT.

I WONDER HOW I KNOW THAT.

AND THEN CAST QUESTION AND ANSWER ASIDE...

...TO CONCEN-TRATE ON THE BATTLE AT HAND.

SHORT, CON-TROLLED BURSTS. AT THEIR LIMBS FIRST, TO IM-MOBILIZE THEM.

THEN, CHEST OR SKULL, TO FINISH THEM OFF.

REMEMBERING ALWAYS TO TAKE CARE NOT TO GET SPLASHED BY THEIR *ACID BLOOD*.

MY MAGAZINE COUNTER DROPS INTO THE LOW DOUBLE-DIGITS...

...SO I LOCK AND LOAD A FRESH CLIP AND SCAN FOR NEW TARGETS.

BIG MAMA ?!

"BI MAM ?!

THERE'S CONCERN IN MY VOICE, ALMOST AS FOR A TRUSTED **FRIEND**.

THERE'S AS LITTLE NEED FOR IT...

...AS FOR ANY HELP

< YOU HAVE A CLEAR SHOT, WHY DON'T YOU *KILL* IT?! >

THUNDERSTRUCK, I'VE NO IDEA. THE THOUGHT NEVER ENTERED MY HEAD.

EVEN THEN, I CAN'T PULL THE TRIGGER.

I TAKE REFUGE FROM MY CONFUSION IN ACTION.

THE BOY DOESN'T NEED ANY ENCOURAGEMENT AS I HUSTLE HIM OFF THE RIDGE.

I WISH I HAD MORE CONFIDENCE IN MY ABILITY TO BRING HIM SAFELY HOME. TO HIS *VIRTUAL* HOME.

< CARYN, *LOOK OUT--* THE MONSTER! >

SLAP!

< NO, PLEASE, *NO!* I'VE DONE YOU NO HARM. WHY ARE YOU DOING THIS? PLEASE, I *BEG* YOU! >

KILL.... IT!

< NO!! >

SQUEEE

SHLUK

NOW IT'S MY TURN TO GO BERSERK.

NOT SIMPLY FOR THE BOY...

... BUT FOR SHARI AND MITCHELL AND THOSE SOLDIERS WHOSE GEAR AND CLOTHES I WEAR.

AND ALL THE OTHER SOULS THIS BUTCHER'S CLAIMED AS TROPHIES. REAL OR IMAGINED.

AND POSSIBLY EVEN, AT THE LAST, FOR MYSELF.

BECAUSE I'M A TROPHY, TOO.

SPLASH!

YARRGH!

DON'T MUCH LIKE THOSE *JELLYFISH*, eh?

LOOKS LIKE THEIR *VENOM* HURT YOU EVEN MORE THAN ME.

POOR BUNNY.

ANY LAST WORDS?

ASH ...?

CARYN!

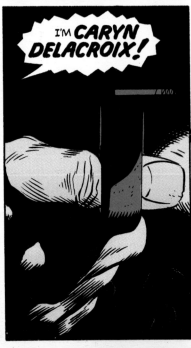

I'M *CARYN DELACROIX!*

BOOM

NEXT: *VIRTUALLY REA*

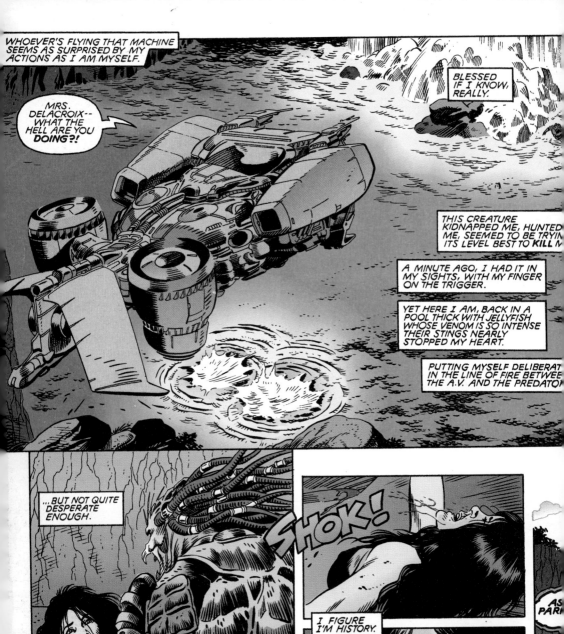

WHOEVER'S FLYING THAT MACHINE SEEMS AS SURPRISED BY MY ACTIONS AS I AM MYSELF.

BLESSED IF I KNOW, REALLY.

MRS. DELACROIX-- WHAT THE HELL ARE YOU *DOING*?!

THIS CREATURE KIDNAPPED ME, HUNTED ME, SEEMED TO BE TRYIN ITS LEVEL BEST TO **KILL** M

A MINUTE AGO, I HAD IT IN MY SIGHTS, WITH MY FINGER ON THE TRIGGER.

YET HERE I AM, BACK IN A POOL THICK WITH JELLYFISH WHOSE VENOM IS SO INTENSE THEIR STINGS NEARLY STOPPED MY HEART.

PUTTING MYSELF DELIBERAT IN THE LINE OF FIRE BETWEE THE A.V. AND THE PREDATOF

...BUT NOT QUITE DESPERATE ENOUGH.

SHOK!

I FIGURE I'M HISTORY.

ASH... PARNALL?

AS PARM

IT SO ALMC HAPP

I MUST BE **MAD**.

I CERTAINLY MUST BE **BLESSED**.

THIS TIME, THE STINGS DON'T HURT. I BARELY FEEL THEIR TOUCH.

NOT SO, THE PREDATOR.

IT HUGS THE SHORE, FAVORING A LEG THAT'S SCARRED WITH FRESH WELTS, CLEARLY IN AGONY.

I'M AMAZED IT CAN MOVE AT ALL...

...UNTIL I SEE WHAT IT'S AFTER.

MY **PULSE RIFLE**!

IN THE CONFUSION, I LOST MY GRIP ON IT.

I MAKE A **DESPERATE** GRAB...

ND I WONDER WE'RE **BOTH** EMENTED.

FLIERS DON'T MUCH LIKE BEING SHOT AT.

WHAM!

STUN GRENADE DID ITS JOB, TOMMY-- THEY'RE **DOWN**!

WATCH THAT **BIG UGLY**, MARIA!

NO PROB, PARTNER. SUCKER AIN'T MOVIN', AIN'T CONSCIOUS.

HOW'S TH MISSUS?

AWAKE BUT FADIN' FAST.

NOT TO WORRY, CARYN. EVERYTHING'S GONNA BE FINE.

WE'RE HERE TO TAKE YO HOME

ASH PARNALL!

ROLL THE CIVILIANS OUTTA HERE, TOMMY!

I'LL HOLD *BIG UGLY* 'TIL THE BACK-UP ARRIVES!

ZARK!

MARIA!

BASTARD!

WHATEVER IT TAKES, YOU'LL *PAY* FOR HER LIFE!

BASTARD...

...YOU'LL PAY!

ASH... PARNALL!

KEEPS... CALLING THAT NAME!

CARYN... OUT OF HERE, NOW!

NO! LUCIEN-- I HAVE TO FIND HIM!

DAMN YOU, WOMAN! THAT MONSTER'S AFTER YOU!

IT'S SLAUGHTERING EVERYONE IN ITS WAY!

YOU'VE GOT TO GO!

MY GOD--

--BIG MAMA, NO!

SHLUK!

MY SKIN-- IT TORE RIGHT OFF!

BUT WHAT'S THIS BODY UNDER-NEATH?!

DAMN YOU, MONSTER! WHY DO YOU KEEP HOUNDING ME?!

WHO AM I SUPPOSED TO BE?!

CARYN... DELA-CROIX!

BLAM!

CARYN?

CARYN?

THAT'S A WRETCHED HABIT, SMOKING.

ESPECIALLY TO EXCESS.

TONIGHT, LUCIEN, I'M IN THE MOOD.

IT'S VERY LATE. WHY DON'T YOU COME TO BED?

I CAN'T SLEEP.

WELL THEN, MY LOVE, WE'LL SIMPLY HAVE TO FIND SOME OTHER WAY...

...TO PAS THE TIM

THIS WASN'T PART OF THE DEAL, MARIA.

WE DID WHAT WAS ASKED, WE GET A FEW DAYS TO LIVE THE HIGH LIFE, NO QUESTIONS, NO GRIEF.

SO WHAT'S THE PROB, TOMMY?

THEY GOT A POOL, I WANT TO SWIM-- Q.E.D.

GIVE IT A REST, WHY DON'TCHA, B'FORE YOU TURN INTO SOME WHINY LITTLE RANDOM!

IT'S NONE OF OUR CONCERN THAT CARYN DELACROI HAS BAD DREAMS HELL, AFTER WHAT SHE'S BEEN THROUGH, WHO WOULDN'T?

HAVE A LITTLE FAITH, SHIROW, WILLYA? I KNOW WHAT I'M DOING.

FAMOUS LAST WORDS, DeMEDICI!

UP YOURS!

THE WOMAN COMES UP OUT OF NOWHERE...

...WITH A STROKE TO MATCH MY OWN...

...AND A GRIN THAT OFFERS AN IRRESISTIBLE CHALLENGE.

HOW IS IT, *SEIGNEUR,* A HIGH-POWERED CORPORATE EXECUTIVE-- *JUNIOR* MEMBER OF THE BOARD AND ALL--

--KNOWS ABOUT THE "CIRCUIT"?

I'M WAITING FOR YOUR ANSWER, WILLY-BOY.

GO TO *HELL!*

THE WOMAN IS ALL SMILES-- SHE COULDN'T APPEAR MORE RELAXED.

IT'S *GISANDE'S* REACTION THAT STARTLES ME, SOMETHING DEEP IN HER EYES I'VE NEVER SEEN BEFORE: *FEAR.*

WHETHER OF THE WOMAN HERSELF OR WHAT SHE SAID, I DON'T KNOW AND I DON'T CARE. THIS HAS GOTTEN FAR ENOUGH OUT OF HAND.

bump

O°OPSIE!

Oh MY *GOODNESS!*

WILLEM, I'M SO TERRIBLY *SORRY*-- I DON'T KNOW HOW I COULD HAVE BEEN SO *CLUMSY!*

GOOD FOR YOU, MISSUS.

MY PARTNER WAS LOOKING TO TAKE THAT YA-YA'S HEAD OFF.

STILL, THE WATER'S DELIGHTFUL.

PERHAPS A SWIM'S JUST WHAT YOU NEED TO COOL YOUR TEMPER.

YOU YOU *YO*

DON'T SAY A WORD, WILLEM, NOT ANOTHER BLOODY WORD!

WHY DIDN'T YOU *DO* SOMETHING? THEY'RE *LAUGHING* AT ME!

YOU GAVE THEM CAUSE.

WATCH YOUR TONGUE, WOMAN!

IS THAT A THREAT, SEIGNEUR?

A REMINDER, GISANDE, THAT YOU DO YOUR JOB-- AND REMEMBER YOUR PLACE.

WILLEM, I HAVE FINISHED SCRIPT REVISIONS AND PRODUCTION COST ESTIMATES ON "REDLANCE."

NOT NOW, TOY.

AS *CHIEF OF PRODUCTION*, YOUR REVIEW AND APPROVAL ARE REQUIRED BEFORE--

FILE IT IN MY BUFFER!

FORGIVE ME, WILLEM, BUT YOUR FATHER HAS TASKED THIS AS A PRIORITY ASSIGNMENT, FOR IMMEDIATE IMPLEMENTATION.

I SAID, I'LL *GET* TO IT! NOW LEAVE US THE HELL *ALONE!*

GOD*DAMN* THAT INFERNAL MACHINE!

NOT ONLY DOES IT LOOK HUMAN, IT'S STARTING TO *ACT* LIKE IT! I SWEAR IT *LIKES* GIVING ME ORDERS!

THAT WOMAN WITH CARYN, AND HER BOYFRIEND-- WHAT HAVE YOU LEARNED?!

SO FAR, NOTHING MORE.

THEN, DO BETTER-- QUICKLY!

I WANT TO KNOW *EVERY-THING* ABOUT THEM, GISANDE, AND MOST ESPECIALLY...

...HOW THEY CAN BE *HURT!*

WHAT'S SHAKIN', MANO?

CARYN--?! MISSUS DELA--?! WHAT THE HELL!?!

BOY, I AM IMPRESSED.

WHATEVER YOU DID TO DESERVE THIS, MORE POWER TO YOU-- 'CAUSE I THINK YOU'RE GONNA NEED IT!

YOU LOOK GRUMPY, SWEETIE.

YOU DON'T LIKE US?

HAT ISN'T--! I'M OT--!

I MEAN--

WHAT THE HELL HAVE YOU TWO GONE AND...

...DONE !?!

GOTCHA, BRIGHT-EYES!

VERY NICE, INDEED.

IT'S NOTHING SPECIAL, REALLY. SOMETHING TOY DESIGNED, A MINIATURIZED VARIANT ON OUR STANDARD IMAGING SYSTEMS.

ONE TALENTED PIECE O' WORK, YOUR COMPUTER.

WHAT ELSE WOULD YOU EXPECT OF HIM? HE'S MONTCALM-DELACROIX'S BRAIN TRUST.

YOU TWO GUYS WERE TALKIN' PRETTY TIGHT, TOMMY. ANYTHING YOU'D CARE TO SHARE?

HE THOUGHT YOU WERE MY TROPHIES.

YOU SHOULD BOTH BE FLATTERED-- THAT'S QUITE A COMPLIMENT.

IT DON'T BOTHER YOU, BEIN' CONSIDERED ESSENTIALLY CHATTEL?

I DON'T KNOW. CAN YOU MISS WHAT YOU NEVER HAD, OR YEARN FOR SOMETHING THAT HAS NO MEANING?

I'M HAPPY, I'M FULFILLED, I LIVE A GOOD LIFE. CLICHÉ AS IT MAY BE, THERE ARE WORSE FATES.

DANCING THE CIRCUIT, FOR EXAMPLE.

WHAT IS THA TOMAS--THE CIRCUIT, I MEAN? WILLEM MENTIONED I BEFORE.

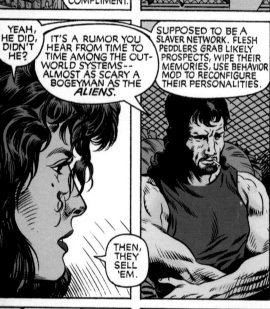

YEAH, HE DID, DIDN'T HE?

IT'S A RUMOR YOU HEAR FROM TIME TO TIME AMONG THE OUT-WORLD SYSTEMS-- ALMOST AS SCARY A BOGEYMAN AS THE ALIENS.

SUPPOSED TO BE A SLAVER NETWORK. FLESH PEDDLERS GRAB LIKELY PROSPECTS, WIPE THEIR MEMORIES, USE BEHAVIOR MOD TO RECONFIGURE THEIR PERSONALITIES.

THEN, THEY SELL 'EM.

WE SAY "RUMOR" BECAUSE NO ONE'S EVER MANAGED TO PROVE ITS EXISTENCE.

THERE ARE ALWAYS THE OCCA-SIONAL ATTEMPTS-- BY COPS OR JOURNALISTS. NOTHING EVER COMES OF 'EM. SOME FOLKS GIVE UP IN FRUSTRATION. OTHERS SIMPLY...

...DISAPPEAR.

HAVE YOU EVE LOOKED

WE'RE NOT COPS. OR JOURNALISTS.

WHAT ARE YOU?

AT THE MOMENT, YOUR GUESTS.

AND WHO KNOWS, MAYBE-- JUST A LITTLE-- FRIENDS.

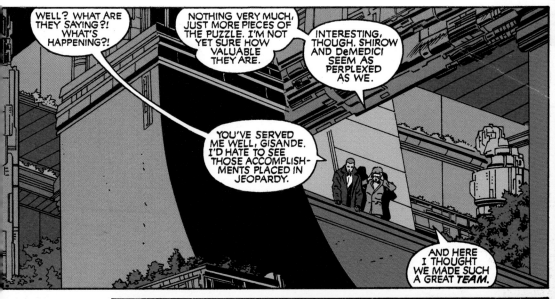

WELL? WHAT ARE THEY SAYING?! WHAT'S HAPPENING?!

NOTHING VERY MUCH, JUST MORE PIECES OF THE PUZZLE. I'M NOT YET SURE HOW VALUABLE THEY ARE.

INTERESTING, THOUGH. SHIROW AND DeMEDICI SEEM AS PERPLEXED AS WE.

YOU'VE SERVED ME WELL, GISANDE. I'D HATE TO SEE THOSE ACCOMPLISHMENTS PLACED IN JEOPARDY.

AND HERE I THOUGHT WE MADE SUCH A GREAT TEAM.

WHAT WAS IT HENRY FORD SAID, IN THE OLD DAYS: "IT'S MY NAME ON THE BUILDING."

NEVER FORGET THAT.

I DON'T, WILLEM.

AND IT'S YOUR FATHER'S NAME.

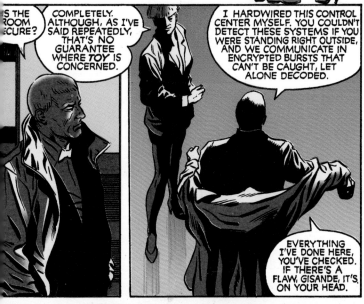

S THE ROOM ECURE?

COMPLETELY. ALTHOUGH, AS I'VE SAID REPEATEDLY, THAT'S NO GUARANTEE WHERE TOY IS CONCERNED.

I HARDWIRED THIS CONTROL CENTER MYSELF. YOU COULDN'T DETECT THESE SYSTEMS IF YOU WERE STANDING RIGHT OUTSIDE, AND WE COMMUNICATE IN ENCRYPTED BURSTS THAT CAN'T BE CAUGHT, LET ALONE DECODED.

EVERYTHING I'VE DONE HERE, YOU'VE CHECKED. IF THERE'S A FLAW, GISANDE, IT'S ON YOUR HEAD.

MANY THANKS, SEIGNEUR, FOR THE VOTE OF CONFIDENCE.

I DIDN'T BRING UP THE SUBJECT.

NOW, PUT DeMATIER ON-LINE.

SALUTATIONS, SEIGNEUR. I AM PLEASED TO REPORT WE ARE PROCEEDING AHEAD OF SCHEDULE.

WITH GOOD FORTUNE, WE SHOULD BE READY TO DECANT THE FIRST TIER WITHIN THE FORTNIGHT.

YOUR SECURITY IS, I ASSUME, ADEQUATE?

THIS IS NO TIME FOR OVER-CONFIDENCE, MESSIEURS, ON ANYONE'S PART.

THE BIO-ENGINEERING PROCEDURES YOU'RE ATTEMPTING, PROFESSOR, ARE TOTALLY FORBIDDEN-- NOT TO MENTION WHAT YOU'RE TRYING TO ACCOMPLISH WITH THEM. OR WHAT YOU'RE USING AS RAW MATERIAL.

THERE IS NO MARGIN FOR ERROR IF ANY HINT OF THIS REACHES THE SECURITATE...

MORE THAN ADEQUATE, MY DEAR.

THERE HAS BEEN NO ERROR, MY DEAR, OF THAT YOU HAVE MY ABSOLUTE ASSURANCE.

TRANSMISSION CLOSED.

HE'S HIDING SOMETHING.

SOMETHING ELSE FOR YOU TO DETERMINE, THEN.

IN THE MEANWHILE, LET'S MOVE ALONG TO THE NEXT ORDER OF BUSINESS.

OPEN A SECURE CHANNEL TO THE CIRCUIT. PROFIT AND LOSS STATEMENTS TO BEGIN, FOLLOWED BY INVENTORY STATUS AND PENDING ORDERS.

WHAT'S THE STATUS OF THAT POLICE INQUIRY, BY THE WAY?

COMPLETELY NEUTRALIZED. TWO INVESTIGATORS ELIMINATED, ONE NOW WORKING FOR US, TWO DANCING THE CIRCUIT.

WE EVEN TURNED A TIDY PROFIT ON THE ENGAGEMENT.

SPLENDID! YOU SHOULD HAVE HAD MORE FAITH IN ME, FATHER. IT WON'T BE LONG NOW BEFORE I'M RUNNING THE CORPORATION...

...AND THERE WON'T BE A BLESSED THING YOU CAN DO ABOUT IT.

I CAN'T SLEEP.

I'M TOO AFRAID OF MY DREAMS.

I NEED A CHANGE OF PACE.

PERHAPS I'LL GO HUNTING.

SNIKT!

I CAN'T SLEEP.

I'M TOO AFRAID OF MY DREAMS.

ABOARD THIS VESSEL, CARYN, I AM EVERY-WHERE.

DO YOU KNOW EVERYTHING, THEN?

I DO MY BEST.

TOY-- AM I INSANE?

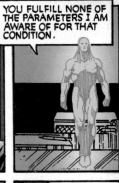

YOU FULFILL NONE OF THE PARAMETERS I AM AWARE OF FOR THAT CONDITION.

I HAVE NIGHT-MARES, TOY.

TO BE TROUBLED IS NOT NECESSARILY TO BE INSANE.

HOW COMFORTING. IS THERE ANY MORE WORD ON MY THERAPIST, DR. JOHANNES?

HE IS STILL... UNAVAILABLE, CARYN.

THEN I'LL JUST HAVE TO WAIT FOR HIM TO COME BACK.

IT IS MY UNDER-STANDING THAT HIS DEPARTURE IS PERMANENT.

SO WHAT DO I DO, THEN?

YOU MIGHT ADDRESS THE CONCERNS PRESENTED IN YOUR DREAMS.

WHAT, THAT I'M BEING HAUNTED BY SOME MONSTER? THAT I KEEP GETTING MYSELF *KILLED*?!

TELL ME, TOY-- MY *VIRTUAL* DUEL IN THE JUNGLE-- WHY DID YOU COME UP WITH SOMETHING SO *AWFUL*?

I HAVE NO ANSWER FOR THAT, CARYN.

I THOUGHT YOU WERE FORBIDDEN TO BRING HARM TO PEOPLE.

THAT IS CORRECT.

MY CORE PROGRAMMING DERIVES FROM THE THREE LAWS OF ROBOTICS POSTULATED IN THE LATE 20th CENTURY BY THE SCIENCE FICTION GRAND MASTER ISAAC ASIMOV:

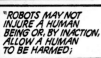

"ROBOTS MAY NOT INJURE A HUMAN BEING OR, BY INACTION, ALLOW A HUMAN TO BE HARMED;

"ROBOTS MUST OBEY HUMANS' ORDERS, UNLESS DOING SO CONFLICTS WITH THE FIRST LAW;

"ROBOTS MUST PRO-TECT THEIR OWN EXISTENCE, UNLESS DOING SO CONFLICTS WITH THE FIRST TWO LAWS."

BUT THE SCENARIO YOU CREATED FOR ME *HAS* DONE ME HARM!

NOT SO, CARYN.

HOW CAN YOU *SAY* THAT--!

OH?!

OW!

AS THE CHAIR OVERBALANCE AND I FALL, I MAKE A REFLEXIVE GRAB FOR THE DESK.

AND PULL THE MAIN DRAWER FREE INSTEAD.

I'M... *BLEEDING!*

THOSE *BLADES!*

THE *MASK!*

ARE THEY *REAL?*

OR IS THIS ANOTHER NIGHTMARE?

WAS THE JUNGLE REAL TOO, TOY?

IS THE *PREDATOR?*

BUT WHY WOULD EVERYONE *LIE* ABOUT IT? WHY GO TO SUCH INCREDIBLE LENGTHS...

...TO MAKE ME BELIEVE IT WAS A FANTASY? WHAT ARE THEY TRYING TO HIDE?

TO ANSWER WOULD POTENTIALLY DO HARM TO THIS CORPORATION, AND MORE IMPORTANTLY, PLACE YOU AT CONSIDERABLE RISK.

THAT IS A VIOLATION OF MY CORE PROGRAMMING.

AND I SUPPOSE I SHOULD BE GRATEFUL.

NEVER MIND. I'LL SIMPLY HAVE TO FIND OUT THE ANSWERS FOR MYSELF.

AND I KNOW JUST WHERE TO BEGIN.

NEXT: *THE GREAT ESCAP*

I WAITED UNTIL SHE UNLOCKED HER DOOR BEFORE MAKING MY MOVE.

VERY PROFESSIONAL. I SURPRISE MYSELF AS MUCH AS I DO HER.

CORPORATE *TROPHIES* AREN'T SUPPOSED TO KNOW HOW TO STAGE AN AMBUSH.

HOW *DARE* YOU?!

WHAT'S THE MEANING OF THIS?!

I'LL ASK THE QUESTIONS.

WILLEM WAS RIGHT, *CARYN*-- YOU *HAVE* GONE MAD!

IN THAT CASE, SINCE I HAVE YOUR GUN, PERHAPS YOU'D BEST *HUMOR* ME.

WHERE IS IT, GISANDE? THE *CREATURE* I FOUGHT IN THE JUNGLE--

--WHAT HAVE YOU *DONE* WITH IT?!

I THOUGHT YOU UNDER-STOOD--

--INASMUCH AS YOUR KIND IS *CAPABLE* OF UNDERSTANDING-- THAT DUEL WAS A *VIRTUAL REALITY* SCENARIO.

IT *NEVER* HAPPENED, CARYN.

YOUR "CREATURE" DOESN'T EXIST.

THEN WHAT THE HELL IS *THIS*--

--A *PROP*?!

YOU KNOW, CARYN, THAT GUN'S MAKING ME AWFULLY *NERVOUS.*

THAT'S THE IDEA.

WHERE DID YOU GET THIS?

WHAT MATTERS IS, I HAVE IT-- THAT AND MORE.

ANSWER MY QUESTION, GISANDE!

WHICH QUESTION WAS THAT, PRAY TELL?

WHAT ARE YOU *DOING?*

SIT BACK DOWN ON THE FLOOR, THIS INSTANT!

I DON'T THINK SO. IT'S VERY UNCOMFORT- ABLE.

I DON'T WANT TO HURT YOU.

AND I RESPECT YOU FOR THAT, TRULY.

BUT LOOK AT YOURSELF, CARYN, LOOK AT THIS SITUATION, HOLDING A GUN, MAKING SUCH THREATS, THIS ISN'T RIGHT, THIS ISN'T *YOU.*

WHERE'S THE *PREDATOR,* SALAZAR?! ANSWER, OR I'LL *SHOOT!*

HOW, MY DEAR? THE GUN ISN'T EVEN *COCKED.*

KLATCH!

I'M SUITABLY IMPRESSED.

STILL, YOUR POSITION WOULD BE HELPED IMMEASUR- ABLY...

...IF THE WEAPON WERE ACTUALLY *LOADED*--

--BOO!

R OUTCRY ARTLES ME.

MY FINGER TIGHTENS CONVULSIVELY ON THE HAIR TRIGGER.

KLIK!

OH DEAR, WHAT A SHAME.

NOW IT'S *MY* TURN!

...BUT SHE'S STILL FAR STRONGER AND FASTER THAN ANY NORMAL HUMAN.

SHE DOESN'T HAVE THE FULL-SPECTRUM ENHANCEMENTS OF A BODY-GUARD OR A STRIKE TROOPER...

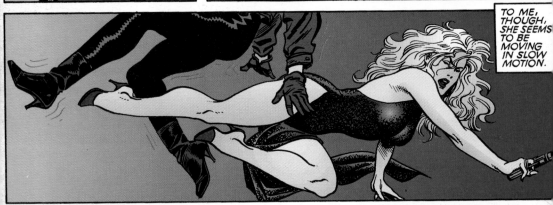

TO ME, THOUGH, SHE SEEMS TO BE MOVING IN SLOW MOTION.

AND FOR HER EVERY ATTACK...

...I HAVE COUNTER.

I FINISH THE FIGHT WITH A GOOD, OLD-FASHIONED ROUND-HOUSE PUNCH TO THE JAW...

KRAK!

...THAT ACTUALLY HURTS ME AS MUCH AS IT DOES HER.

I'VE NEVER BEEN IN A FIGHT BEFORE, NOT LIKE THIS...

...NOT THAT I CAN REMEMBER.

I'M SHAKING AS SHE FALLS.

I CAN'T BELIEVE I'VE WON.

I HALF EXPECT HER TO LEAP UP AND GO FOR MY THROAT.

BUT SHE DOESN'T STIR.

MY GOD.

MIGOD MIGOD MIGOD MIGOD

I'M CRYING. I WANT TO BE SICK.

I WANT TO BE IN MY OWN BED, WITH NO THOUGHTS IN MY HEAD BUT HOW BEST TO PLEASE MY BELOVED LUCIEN.

ANYWHERE BUT HERE, DOING ANYTHING BUT THIS.

IT SHOULDN'T BE POSSIBLE.

THERE'S NOTHING IN MY TRAINING, NOTHING IN MY GENETICS...

...BUT IT'S HAPPENING NONETHELESS.

JUST LIKE IN THE JUNGLE.

AND SOME-HOW, IT'S ALL BOUND UP WITH THE *MONSTER* FROM MY NIGHT-MARES.

THE CREATURE THAT WORE THIS *MASK*.

SO TELL ME, UGLY-- WHERE THE HELL *ARE* YOU-- *eh?!*

SOME-THING'S BLINKING INSIDE...

GASP?!

WELL!

AN INTERNAL *HOLOGRAPHIC DISPLAY*. VOICE-ACTIVATED. *VERY* SOPHISTI-CATED.

THE *ICON* REPRESENTS THE PREDATOR, THE ARROW POINTS ME IN THE RIGHT DIRECTION.

BUT I CAN'T GO HUNTING DRESSED LIKE THIS.

GISANDE'S THE FIGHTER BY TRADE. WE'RE PRETTY MUCH THE SAME SIZE. I'M SURE SHE HAS SOME-THING APPROPRIATE...

...FOR *EVERY* OCCASION, IT APPEARS.

AND I THOUGHT *MY* CLOSET WAS RUDE.

WHY, MS. SALAZAR, IN YOUR SECRET HEART OF HEARTS...

...WOULD YOU RATHER BE A *TROPHY?*

PERHAPS, BY TRADING COSTUMES, WE'LL TRADE *ROLES* AS WELL.

THE LUNGS APPARENTLY EVOLVED IN A RADICALLY DIFFERENT ECOSYSTEM. THEY FUNCTION IN OUR OXYGEN ATMOSPHERE ONLY WITH GREAT DIFFICULTY.

HENCE, THE FACE MASK, TO PROVIDE PROPER "AIR" TO BREATHE.

AND THIS IS NOT AN "IT," WILLEM. THE CREATURE IS FEMALE.

I STAND CORRECTED.

WE WANT HER.

WHEN CAN SHE BE TRANSPORTED TO OUR RESEARCH FACILITY?

ARE YOU SURE THAT'S WISE?

THERE IS A GREAT DEAL OF ATTENTION BEING FOCUSED ON THAT CREATURE-- EVEN MY FATHER'S INVOLVED.

ANY PRECIPITATE ACTION ON OUR PART COULD NOT ONLY PUT THE PROJECT IN JEOPARDY, BUT OUR LIVES!

SUCH SOLICITOUS REGARD FOR OUR WELFARE. WE ARE DEEPLY TOUCHED.

BUT WE MUST HAVE HER, WILLEM.

ESPECIALLY IF SHE IS STILL FERTILE.

I DON'T KNOW, PROFESSOR-- THE RISK--!

IS TOO GREAT?

HOW COMMENDABLY CAUTIOUS, DEAR BOY. WE ARE SURE YOUR PRECIOUS GISANDE WOULD WHOLEHEARTEDLY APPROVE.

SHE'S MY SECURITY. IT'S HER FUNCTION.

BORN AND BRED FOR THE ROLE, JUST AS A TROPHY WIFE IS FOR HERS.

BUT, WILLEM, FROM THE GREATEST RISK COMES THE GREATEST REWARD.

YOU'VE HAZARDED SO MUCH ALREADY, AND COME SO FAR-- WHAT'S ONE STEP MORE?

THIS IS A HUGE CORPORATION, AND YOU ARE ONE OF ITS MOST POWERFUL EXECUTIVES, SECOND ONLY TO YOUR FATHER.

IF THE CREATURE'S LOST, WHO WILL MISS HER? IF SHE'S MISSED, WHO CAN FIND HER? IF SHE CAN'T BE FOUND...

...HOW LONG BEFORE SHE'S FORGOTTEN?

ARRANGEMENTS WILL BE MADE.

YOU'LL BE NOTIFIED WHEN WE'RE READY.

HOPEFULLY, NOT FOR VERY LONG.

WE SHALL BE WAITING, DEAR BOY.

NEVER FORGET, PROFESSOR-- YOU EXECUTE POLICY.

I MAKE IT!

OF COURSE, SEIGNEUR. THAT GOES WITHOUT SAYING, SEIGNEUR. YOUR MOST HUMBLE AND ABJECT SERVANT EAGERLY AWAITS YOUR NEXT CALL, SEIGNEUR...

...AND YOUR NEXT COMMAND.

UNTIL THEN, DEAR BOY...

DAMN YOU, GISANDE!

WHERE THE HELL ARE YOU WHEN I NEED YOU MOST?!

I WONDER WHAT'S SCARIER-- THAT I'M SO GOOD TO BEGIN WITH...

...OR THAT I'M GETTING *BETTER* AS I GO ALONG?

BipBap BipBap

Beep

STAND AWAY FROM THE TABLE, GENTLEMEN.

FACES TO THE WALL, PLEASE, AND HANDS WHERE I CAN SEE THEM.

DO AS SHE SAYS.

THAT'S A MARINE *AUTOFIRE.* TWO HUNDRED ROUNDS OF TEN-MILLIMETER AMMUNITION. SHE COULD CUT US IN HALF WITH A HICCUP.

I COULDN'T HAVE PUT IT BETTER MY-SELF. THE TECHS DON'T KNOW ME, BUT THEY RESPECT THE WEAPON. THEY DO AS THEY'RE TOLD.

--YOU *ARE* REAL. ND ALL THE REST, O, NO DOUBT.

HIS IS *YOURS,* I THINK.

UESTION IS, HO THE HELL RE YOU...

ND HAT DO U WANT TH ME?!

WHAT... DO YOU WANT... WITH ME?

SUPERB MIMICRY-- BUT A BIT MORE ELOQUENCE WOULD BE USEFUL.

A BIT MORE... ELOQUENCE... WOULD BE USEFUL--

--ASH... PARNALL!

AT LAST, THE NAME TO CONJURE WITH.

BUT CAN YOU TELL ME WHAT IT *MEANS?*

I OUGHT TO HAVE MY SKULL POPPED, DeMEDICI-- THE THINGS I LET YOU BROWBEAT ME INTO.

NICE TALK.

I GOT INSTINCTS, SHIROW-- IS THAT A CRIME?

YOU'RE JUST CRABBY 'CAUSE YOU CAN'T PICK THE LOCK.

YOU THINK YOU CAN DO BETTER, DeMEDICI?

JEEZ LOU-EEZ! SHOULD'A KNOWN FROM THE START-- A GIRL WANTS A THING DONE RIGHT...

KICK!

...SHE'S SIMPLY GOTTA DO IT HERSELF!

I HATE IT WHEN YOU DO STUFF LIKE THIS.

ONLY 'CAUSE IT ALWAYS WORKS

HEY, IS IT MY FAULT YOU NEVER STAY CURRENT WITH THE LITERATURE?

SCORE ONE FOR INSTINCTS.

SOMEONE WAS IN A FIGHT HERE.

WHICH WOULD EXPLAIN WHY MS. SALAZAR HASN'T BEEN ANSWERING OUR CALLS.

LIVING ROOM'S CLEAR

YOU SAID SHE JUST DIDN'T LIKE US.

SHE DOESN'T.

TOMMY-- NEXT DOOR!

IF IT'S HER, YOU THINK SHE'LL APPRECIATE OUR COMING TO HER RESCUE?

ONLY ONE WAY TO FIND OUT.

WHAT D'YOU SEE?

Oh, TOMMY--

-- oh, TOMMY--

--WE'R DOOM

MS. SALAZAR--

-- HAVE WE COME AT A BAD TIME?

GUESS NOT.

HAT BLOODY, EN-ENGINEERED *BITCH!*

DON'TCHA JUST *HATE* IT WHEN THEY LOVE YA AN' LEAVE YA?

BY ALL THAT'S HOLY, I'LL HAVE HER *HEART!*

GO TO HELL, DeMEDICI.

SECURITY CENTRAL!

SEC-CEN ON-LINE...

...CHIEF?!

PUT OUT A SHIPWIDE *ALL-POINTS* ALERT FOR *CARYN DELACROIX.*

THE BOSS'S WIFE?

ARE YOU RECEIVING ME DOWN THERE?!

AVE YOU ALL GONE AF AS WELL AS WITLESS?!

HAT THE LL ARE YOU TARING AT?!

OTHING, A'AM, OTHING ALL.

AND SEND A *FLASH TEAM* TO THE LAB FACILITY, TO SECURE THE UNCLASSIFIED *EXOTIC.*

TELL THEM I'M ON MY WAY. SHIROW AND DeMEDICI, YOU'RE WITH ME.

MOVE, PEOPLE! LIKE YOU'VE GOT A BLOODY *PURPOSE!*

CASUALTIES IN THE LAB.

SEARCH TEAMS FANNING OUT FROM THAT NEXUS-- THEY'RE REPORTING NEGATIVE CONTACT ON ANY LOCAL SCANS.

I'D FEEL A WHOLE LOT BETTER, CHIEF, IF *TOY* COULD PINPOINT THE CRITTER'S LOCATION. OR MRS. DELACROIX'S.

BITCH OF A TIME TO DISCOVER YOUR PET PRIME COMPUTER, IT'S GOT LIMITATIONS-- HEAR WHAT I'M SAYIN'?

I AND EVERY OTHER SOUL IN EARSHOT.

IT'S AN INCONVENIENCE, DeMEDICI, NOTHING MORE. WE'LL MANAGE WITHOUT.

ALL TEAMS, REPORT BY SECTION.

RICO AN' JULES CHIEF, IN SHUTTLE BAY DELTA. WE GO NADA ON OUR TRACK, BY SIGHT OR SCAN.

BE CAREFUL. THE *EXOTIC* IS ARMED AND TO BE CONSIDERED AN *ULTIMATE HAZARD.*

"ULTIMATE," MY KEISTER. ONLY *BUGS'RE* THAT NASTY, AN' WE NAILED OUR SHARE O' THEM JUS' FINE.

BUT SPEAKIN' O' "FINE"--YOU HEAR WHAT'S TALKIN' AT SECURITY CENTRAL, RICO?

OUR BOSS BITCH, LOOKIN' SO RIGHT, SO RUDE, SO *WICKED.*

AN' BEST OF ALL, THOSE *REMF* LAMES GOT HER ON *TAPE!*

TRUST ME, PARTNER, I PUT IN AN ORDER FOR YOU, TOO.

I MEAN, WHO'D'A THOUGHT THE "ICE QUEEN" HAD IT IN HER--

--TO TURN O SO UTTE AN' TOTA TO DI FOR

...UTTERLY AND TOTALLY... TO DIE FOR!

ABSOLUTELY!

YO, RICO!

CUT IT OUT WITH THE GAMES, WOMAN-- WE'RE ONNA JOB HERE. THIS IS...

...SERIOUS...

I TRIED.

TO STOP THIS, YELL A WARNING, DO SOMETHING!

BUT I'M LITTLE MORE THAN A DOLL IN ITS HANDS.

EVEN ARMED AND ARMORED TROOPERS AREN'T MUCH BETTER.

HY, DAMN YOU-- HY'D YOU HAVE KILL THEM?!

WE'RE ONNA JOB HERE.

THIS... IS... SERIOUS.

PTINK

I'M GRABBED BY THE SCRUFF OF THE NECK AND HUSTLED ALONG SO FAST MY FEET BARELY TOUCH THE FLOOR.

BUT AS WE EMERGE FROM COVER...

THERE THEY ARE!

HOLD YOUR FIRE, SALAZAR-- YOU'LL HIT THE WOMAN!

LIKE I CARE?

KCHOW!

I DIDN'T DO THAT!

THE GRENADES RUPTURE THE FUEL CELLS OF A PARKED SHUTTLE, FLOODING THE BAY WITH A SEA OF FIRE, ONE BLAST TRIGGERING ANOTHER, UNTIL...

THE WALL'S BUCKLING!

GISANDE-- THE CATWALK!

HANG ON, I'M COMING!

MARIA, ANCHOR ME SO I CAN REACH!

DROP THE RIFLE, WOMAN! TAKE MY HAND!

I'VE GOT A CLEAR SHOT!

BLAM

THE PREDATOR FALLS LIKE IT'S BEEN HIT BY A SLEDGE-HAMMER.

IT'S A PERFECT TARGET.

BUT GISANDE NEVER HAS THE CHANCE TO TAKE ADVANTAGE.

YARRRGH

BOOM

SHIROW, I'M BURNING! I'M BURNING

TOMMY--! USE YOUR JACKET, MARIA! SMOTHER THE FLAMES!

CLEAR ME SOME ROOM, SO I CAN GET HER AWAY FROM THE EDGE.

THE FLAMES ARE STARTING TO COOK THE CATWALK!

IS SHE ALIVE?

SHE'S A FIGHTER, LIKE YOU.

CENTRAL-- DELTA BAY, SKYCROSS 12-CHARLEY, I'VE GOT A MAJOR BURN CASE! I NEED A MEDEVAC TRAUMA TEAM! NOW!

DAMMIT, MARIA, GET *AWAY* FROM THERE!

WHAT THE HELL ARE YOU DOING-- YOU WANT TO FRY, TOO?!

OUR "EXOTIC" DON'T KNOW WHEN TO QUIT, TOMMY!

I FIGURE I'LL GIVE IT A LITTLE MOR *PERSUADING*!

I HEAR MARIA, CALLING ON ME TO *GET AWAY*.

THE PREDATOR GLARES AT ME LIKE A FRIEND BETRA

IT'S HORRIBLY WOUNDED-- THE FLOOR GLEAMS WITH ITS EMERALD BLOOD-- BUT IT REFUSES TO SURRENDER.

BLAM! BLAM!

FAR AS YOU GO, UGLY!

CRITTER AIN'T TAKIN' THE HINT, TOMMY. I GOT NO CHOICE BUT TO DRILL IT.

WHATEVER, DO IT FAST!

METAL'S GETTING TOO HOT FOR US TO STAY.

NO!

LEAVE IT ALONE! LET IT *GO*!

WE GOT A *PROBLEM*.

THE WOMAN'S *DEMENTED*!

ONLY WAY TO FINISH THE CRITTER IS TO DROP HER FIRST.

DAMN!

THAT'S *IT,* DeMEDICI! WE'RE *THROUGH* HERE!

FORGET THE EXOTIC!

WE DON'T SCRAMBLE-- *RIGHT NOW*-- WE'LL BE FRIED AS BADLY AS THE CHIEF HERE!

ANOTHER SECOND, TOMMY, THAT'S ALL I NEEDED.

YOU DIDN'T HAVE IT, MARIA, AND THAT'S THE PLAIN FACT OF THE MATTER.

SO LET IT GO, AND WAIT FOR ANOTHER CHANCE.

WHERE'S THE TRAUMA TEAM?! I'VE GOT A *CASUALTY* HERE!

MAJOR SHIROW! COLONEL DeMEDICI!

WHAT'S HAPPENED TO CARYN?!

WHERE'S MY WIFE?!

VASH*TOOM!*

SIGNEUR! RADAR TRACKING LOST THE TARGET IN GROUND CLUTTER. THE PURSUIT FLIGHT NEVER ACHIEVED A SOLID INTERCEPT.

THE *EXOTIC* DID THIS?

NOT HARDLY.

SANDE AND BOTH PUT OUNDS INTO TS CHEST.

IF THAT WASN'T ENOUGH, IT'S THE WRONG SIZE FOR A SHUTTLE COCKPIT.

IT COULD MAYBE HANDLE THE CONTROLS WELL ENOUGH TO FLY, BUT NOT TO EXECUTE THE KIND OF MANEUVERS NECESSARY TO LOSE YOUR INTERCEPTORS.

ONLY ONE OTHER CANDIDATE, *SEIGNEUR.*

DON'T BE ABSURD!

YOUR ANALYSIS IS FAULTY, COLONEL. CARYN CAN'T FLY. THERE MUST BE SOME OTHER EXPLANATION.

IF YOU SAY SO.

I WANT MY WIFE BACK, MAJOR. ALIVE AND WHOLE.

THE CREATURE AS WELL, IF THAT CAN BE MANAGED, BUT CARYN'S RETURN HAS *ABSOLUTE PRIORITY.*

TO THAT PURPOSE, I WILL PROVIDE YOU WITH ALL THE RESOURCES OF THIS CORPORATION.

IN RETURN, I WILL ACCEPT NEITHER EXCUSES NOR FAILURE.

I TAKE IT, *SEIGNEUR,* WE DON'T HAVE A CHOICE.

EVERYONE HAS A CHOICE, MAJOR.

THE TRICK IS MAKING THE *RIGHT* ONE.

ANOTHER DAWN. ANOTHER SET OF SKILLS.

I DON'T NEED NIGHTMARES ANYMORE TO SCARE ME SILLY.

KENNE[DY] SPACE CENTER

CAPE CANAVERAL, FLORIDA

[U]SA

LIFE DOES THAT NOW, ALL BY ITSELF.

I BANDAGED THE PREDATOR...

...AS BEST I COULD, USING THE SHUTTLE MEDIKIT.

IT'S A MIRACLE SHE'S STILL ALIVE.

JUDGING FROM THE FRESH BLOODSTAINS, THOUGH, SHE WON'T BE FOR MUCH LONGE[R]

SHE CAN BARELY STAND. SHE NEEDS ME NOW MORE THAN EVER.

BUT ONCE WE'RE ABOARD HER SHIP-- AND HOW DO I KNOW, SO INSTANTLY AND INSTINCTIVELY, THAT'S WHAT IT IS--

--WHAT THEN?

ONLY ONE WAY TO FIND OUT.

Roadtrip

THE VIEW TAKES MY BREATH AWAY.

...ha--?! **MY FACE-- THERE'S SOMETHING ON MY FACE!**

IT'S A MASK!

I'M WEARING A MASK.

WHY CAN'T I MOVE?

THE PREDATOR-- GOT TO GET HER OFF ME!

MY GOD! SHE WEIGHS A BLOODY TON!

THAT'S ALL I CAN MANAGE FOR A WHILE.

THE MASK PROVIDES ALL THE AIR I NEED, BUT IT CAN'T DO ANYTHING ABOUT THE DAMAGE ALREADY DONE.

I ACHE SO MUCH INSIDE I ONLY DARE TRY THE SHALLOWEST OF GASPS. HEAVEN KNOWS HOW BADLY MY LUNGS ARE SCARRED.

THE PREDATOR ISN'T BREATHING MUCH BETTER, AND SHE'S LOST A LOT MORE BLOOD.

DON'T HAVE TO LOOK FAR TO SEE WHERE SHE GOT THE MASK.

THIS ISN'T PART OF HER TROPHY WALL.

IT'S RACKED WITH OTHER SUITS OF ARMOR ...

BUT THIS IS MUCH SMALLER ...

...SMALLER EVEN THAN ME.

ASH! ASH PARNALL!

ARE YOU HERE? YOUR FRIEND'S BADLY HURT, AND I DON'T KNOW HOW TO SAVE HER!

ANSWER ME, DAMN YOU! I NEED YOUR HELP!

AND IN HER WAY, SHE DOES.

IT'S A *CADUCEUS*, FLOATING RIGHT BEFORE MY EYES, THANKS TO SOME SORT OF HOLOGRAPHIC IMAGING DISPLAY INTEGRATED RIGHT INTO THE MASK.

IT ONLY APPEARS WHEN I LOOK IN A CERTAIN DIRECTION.

AND LEADS ME TO SOME SORT OF COCOON.

THERE'S A CONTROL PANEL.

WITH INSTRUCTIONS. WRITTEN IN PICTOGRAPHS.

FIGURING WHAT TO DO, THAT'S EASY.

GETTING THE PREDATOR OVER THERE, *THAT'S* THE CHALLENGE.

IN YOU GO, BIG MAMA!

PLEASANT DREAMS!

I ALMOST WISH I HAD ONE OF THESE *AUTO-DOCS* FOR MYSELF.

BUT THERE'S A LOT LESS PAIN INSIDE ME THAN BEFORE, AND NO WEAKNESS TO MY MOVEMENTS-- ALTHOUGH MY VOICE SEEMS TO HAVE DROPPED AN OCTAVE AND GONE ALL HUSKY.

IN A SENSE I'M NOT SURPRISED. TOY BUILT ME WELL.

FUNDAMENTALLY, I'M AS *HUMAN* AS ANYONE ELSE-- ONLY I WAS SHAPED ALMOST FROM THE MOMENT OF CONCEPTION BY MONTCALM-DELACROIX'S *MASTER* COMPUTER.

GENETICALLY ENGINEERED TO BE *PERFECT.*

JUST LIKE TOY HIM-SELF.

ONLY I'M *NOT,* ANYMORE.

I DON'T LIKE THE IMPLICATIONS OF THAT TRAIN OF THOUGHT.

I DECIDE TO GO EXPLORING INSTEAD.

IT'S A BIG SHIP--SHOULD KEEP ME OCCUPIED AWHILE.

AT FIRST GLANCE, WE SEEM SO MUCH LIKE, THE PREDATOR AND I.

ANOTHER PICTO-GRAPH!

THE PREDATOR'S FACE.

HER QUARTERS, MAYBE?

TWO ARMS, TWO LEGS, STANDING ERECT WITH THE HEAD ATOP A CENTRAL TORSO. SHE USES HUMAN WEAPONS --I CAN EVIDENTLY WEAR HER GEAR.

KLAKT

BUT EVERY SO OFTEN, I FIND MYSELF REMINDED OF HOW TRULY ALIEN WE ARE.

WHRUMM

SORT OF THE SAME WAY I'M COMING TO FEEL ABOUT MYSELF.

I'M A TROPHY WIFE, THE IDEAL CONSORT, DESIGNED FOR LOVE NOT WAR.

YET I HANDLE THIS PULSE RIFLE AS THOUGH I'VE BEEN DOING IT MY ENTIRE LIFE.

AND I SCOUT THE VESSEL WITH A COMBAT TROOPER'S BATTLE-HONED SKILL.

ONLY ONE OTHER COMPARTMENT SHOWS A SIGN OF BEING OCCUPIED.

A HUMAN FACE, ONE THAT HAUNTS MY DREAMS.

ASH PARNALL?

THE ROOM'S NEAT, BUT IT'S OBVIOUS THAT NO ONE'S BEEN IN HERE FOR AGES.

THE CLOTHES I FIND ARE MILITARY.

AND THE ALL TOO SMALL FOR ME.

I DON'T MUCH MIND-- I WOULDN'T WEAR THEM IF I COULD.

I'M A TROPHY-- I WEAR ONLY THE BEST.

THESE MAY BE PRACTICAL AND COMFORTABLE, BUT THEY HAVE ALL THE STYLE OF A DEAD BRICK.

WHAT BROUGHT YOU TOGETHER, ASH...

...YOU AND THE PREDATOR'

WHEN I THINK OF HER, IT'S NATURAL TO CALL HER "BIG MAMA."

ARE YOU TWO SOMEHOW RELATED?

ARE WE?

IS THAT WHY I'M INVOLVED?

ONE PICTURE'S OBVIOUSLY FAMILY-- THE RESEMBLANCE IS EASY TO SEE.

THE PHOTO'S OLD.

THE OTHER'S STAINED.

WITH TEARS.

AND BLOOD.

EVENTUALLY, I MAKE MY WAY TO THE **FLIGHT DECK.**

KLEK

FWOOSH!

AIR!

WITH A METHANE UNDERTASTE, TRUE, BUT SAFE ENOUGH TO BREATHE. I'LL SETTLE FOR THAT.

[Y]OU'RE VERY [G]OOD, ASH...

...WHOEVER THE HELL YOU ARE.

[FI]RST, YOU [FI]GURE OUT [H]OW TO [FL]Y THIS [B]UCKET.

AND THEN YOU COME UP WITH A WAY TO PASS ALONG THAT INFORMATION TO WHO-EVER COMES ABOARD.

DOESN'T MATTER IF THEY DON'T SPEAK YOUR LANGUAGE, DOESN'T EVEN MATTER IF THEY'RE ILLITERATE...

...YOU MADE IT SIMPLE ENOUGH FOR **ANYONE** TO PUZZLE OUT.

ONLY ONE PROBLEM, I'M AFRAID.

NOW THAT I'M BLESSED WITH ALL THIS KNOWLEDGE--

--WHAT THE HELL AM I SUPPOSED TO **DO** WITH IT?!

TRUTH TO TELL, WE DIDN'T EXPECT TO SEE YOU AGAIN.

TRUTH TO TELL, NEITHER DID I.

THE DOC SAID YOUR WOUNDS WERE FATAL.

MY DESIGNERS BUILT ME BETTER THAN THEY KNEW. I HEAL FAST. AND VERY WELL.

BIOMECH ENHANCEMENTS? YOU'RE A *SYNTHETIC?*

GOOD GRACIOUS, NO. NOTHING SO CLUMSY.

I'M A MIX OF NANO-TECHNOLOGY AND DESIGNER GENES, TO OPTIMIZE MY ABILITIES IN MY CHOSEN PROFESSION. AMONG OTHER THINGS, A *SECURITY CHIEF* NEEDS TO BE ABLE TO WITHSTAND SERIOUS PUNISHMENT.

IT'S A FAIRLY REVOLUTIONARY PROCESS--*TOY'S* DOING--AN OUT-GROWTH OF THE WORK THAT WENT INTO CREATING THE *TROPHIE*

THAT'S ONE TALENTED COMPUTER.

YOU DON'T SOUND CONVINCED.

TOY CONTROLS EVERY ASPECT OF LIFE ABOARD THE SKYLINER-- EVERYBODY CON-FIRMS THAT.

YET CARYN *WAS* ABLE TO EFFECT THE RESCUE OF THAT CREATURE WITHOUT TOY SOUNDING AN ALARM OR TAKING THE SLIGHTEST EFFORT TO STOP HER.

HEAVEN FORFEND! COULD IT BE THAT TOY ISN'T QUITE AS *PERFECT* AS ADVERTISED?

YOU ASK ME, THE *HUMILITY* MIGHT DO HIM SOME GOOD.

CONSIDERING THE POWER [HE] WIELDS OVER THE [SKYLINER'S] OPERATION, [DOESN'T] THAT [CONCERN] YOU?

LIBERTÉ ISN'T A WARSHIP, MARIA, AND TOY ISN'T A BATTLE NETWORK. MONTCALM-DELACROIX IS AN *ENTERTAINMENT* CONGLOMERATE. BASICALLY, TOY'S ROLE IS TO HELP MAKE *MOVIES*.

ALWAYS ASSUMING HE ISN'T WORKING ON A SURPRISE SCENARIO ALL HIS OWN.

IMPOSSIBLE. FOR ALL HIS SOPHISTI-CATION, TOY IS STILL ONLY A COMPUTER. HE'S LIMITED BY HIS CORE PROGRAMMING.

IF YOU SAY SO.

YO, MARIA, YOU AREN'T GOING TO BELIEVE WHO JUST WALTZED ABOARD.

YO, SHIROW, CLEAR YOUR PEEPS, M'MAN, AN' SWEEP THE FIELD. WHO YOU THINK I GOT SITTIN' UP HERE WITH ME?

SHE JUST BROUGHT OUR ORDERS.

I KNOW. I JUST SCANNED THE COPY DOWNLOADED INTO MY BUFFER. IT SAYS SHE'S PART OF THE TEAM.

WE WORK ALONE, MS. SALAZAR.

SO I TOLD LUCIEN.

AT LONG LAST, I WAS ALLOWED TO SEE YOUR DOSSIERS. I WAS IMPRESSED. I WAS ALSO OVER-RULED.

BOTH OF YOU HAVE TO UNDERSTAND. *LUCIEN DELACROIX* IS HEAD OF THIS CORPORATION. YOU HAVE NO IDEA OF THE EXTENT OF HIS POWER. AND YOU REALLY DON'T WANT TO FIND OUT.

HE WANTS HIS TROPHY BACK-- NO QUESTIONS, NO EXCUSES --AND HE'S PREPARED TO DO WHATEVER'S NECESSARY TO ACHIEVE THAT GOAL.

IF WE WANT OUR LIVES BACK, FREE AND CLEAR...

...THEN WE DO AS WE'RE TOLD. AND PRAY WE'RE NOT AL-READY *TOO LATE*.

W. WOOD SPACECRAFT CO.

SKYLINER
LIBERTÉ
TO GATEWAY
TRAFFIC
CONTROL--

--NOW
DEPARTING
LOW EARTH
ORBIT FOR
UPPER
ATMOSPHERE.
ALL SYSTEMS
NOMINAL.

EMERGENCY HATCH

PROFESSOR DeMATIER--
WHAT THE *DEVIL*--?!

AND A VERY GOOD
EVENING TO YOU,
TOO, DEAR BOY.

HOW
DID YOU GET
IN HERE?!

WE DO BELIEVE
THE DOOR WAS
OPEN.

MY DOOR
IS *NEVER*
OPEN--

--WHAT'S
WRONG,
HERE?!
WHY
CAN'T I
MOVE?!

NOT TO WORRY, DEAR
BOY. MERELY A MINOR--
AND TRANSITORY--
INHIBITION OF THE
VOLUNTARY NERVOUS
SYSTEM.

YOU'LL BE
UP AND
AROUND IN
NO TIME.

UNTIL THEN,
HOWEVER,
DON'T BOTHER
TRYING TO
MOVE. YOU
CAN'T.

DAMN YOU, PROFESSOR, THIS ISN'T FUNNY!

QUITE SO.

IF THE *SECURITATE* WERE TO FIND YOU--!

DEAR, *DEAR* BOY, THE VERY FACT THAT WE ARE *HERE*, SHARING YOUR COMPANY-- THE *FLESH*, SO TO SPEAK--

SHOULD BE MOST ELOQUENT TESTIMONY TO THE SKILL OF YOUR CORPORATE SECURITY SERVICES.

NOT TO MENTION YOUR VAUNTED HOUSE COMPUTER, THE EVER-UBIQUITOUS *TOY*.

WHAT DO YOU WANT? WHY HAVE YOU DONE THIS?

WEREN'T YOU LISTENING WHEN LAST WE SPOKE? WAS IT SO DIFFICULT A THING I ASKED OF YOU?

YOU ASSURED ME IT COULD BE DONE. YET... DO WE HAVE OUR PREDATOR?

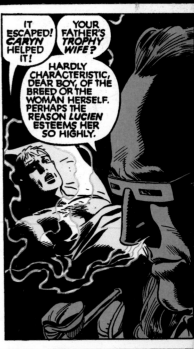

IT ESCAPED! *CARYN* HELPED IT!

YOUR FATHER'S *TROPHY WIFE*?

HARDLY CHARACTERISTIC, DEAR BOY, OF THE BREED OR THE WOMAN HERSELF. PERHAPS THE REASON *LUCIEN* ESTEEMS HER SO HIGHLY.

SPEAKING OF WOMEN, DEAR BOY, WERE WE NOT ALSO PROMISED-- FROM THE VERY INCEPTION OF OUR RELATIONSHIP-- THE USE OF YOUR ILLUSTRIOUS COMPEER, MS. *SALAZAR*, ONCE HER USE-FULNESS TO THE PROJECT CAME TO AN END?

MY-- MY FATHER-- MY FATHER HAD AN *ASSIGNMENT* FOR HER.

WILLEM, DEAR, *DEAR* WILLEM, WHAT KIND OF FOOL DO YOU TAKE US FOR, HMMM?

WE SAW THE TAPES. IT'S A MIRACLE SHE SURVIVED THE INITIAL EXPLOSION-- SHE SHOULD HAVE DIED RIGHT THEN AND THERE-- YET NOW YOU INSIST THAT SHE'S RECOVERED SUFFICIENTLY TO GO GALLIVANTING OFF ON SOME ADVENTURE?

A SUBJECT WITH SUCH *ENHANCE-MENTS* WOULD HAVE BEEN *INVALUABLE* TO US.

I *DIDN'T KNOW* SHE HAD THEM!

DEAR BOY, ON THE BASIS OF YOUR *COMMIT-MENTS*, EVENTS HAVE BEEN SET IN MOTION.

THEY CANNOT BE SET ASIDE SIMPLY BECAUSE YOU HAVE *FAILED* TO FULFILL THEM.

WHAT ARE YOU TALKING ABOUT?! WHAT DO YOU *MEAN*?!

THINK OF IT AS AN END TO SUFFERING.

A *TRANS-FIGURATION* OF THE FLESH TO A MORE GLORIOUS STATE OF BEING.

FOR THE LOVE OF *GOD*, DeMATIER!

IT IS FOR *LOVE* THAT WE OFFER THIS SACRAMENT, DEAR BOY.

SOMEONE-- ANYONE-- HELP ME!

THINK OF IT, WILLEM-- STRENGTH BEYOND IMAGINA-TION, COUPLED WITH A BEAUTY UNLIKE ANY CONCEIVED OF. UNIQUE AND *IMMORTAL*.

THEY CAN'T HEAR YOU WILLEM. NO ONE WILL COME.

LEAST OF ALL YOUR FATHER'S *ELECTRONIC AMANUENSIS*.

TOY!

PROFESSOR, PLEASE, DON'T DO THIS. I THOUGHT WE WERE PARTNERS-- I THOUGHT WE WERE *FRIENDS*!

WHY ARE YOU *DOING* THIS?!

REGRETTABLY, DEAR BOY, WE HAVE RUN INTO SOMETHING OF A ROADBLOCK WITH THE PROJECT. WE HAVE BECOME QUITE PROFICIENT IN THE PRODUCTION OF *DRONES*.

BUT, OF COURSE, THEY'RE ALL *MULES*. THEY CANNOT REPRODUCE.

FOR THAT, WE REQUIRE A *QUEEN*.

NO!

IS ANYTHING *AMISS*, WILLEM?

SCAN THE SUITE, *TOY!* IS THERE ANY SIGN OF *INTRUDERS*?

NOT IN THE SLIGHTEST. ALL HEREIN IS AS IT *SHOULD* BE.

SHALL I SUMMON OFFICERS OF THE *SECURITATE* TO CONDUCT A FURTHER INSPECTION?

NO. NO. THAT WON'T BE NECESSARY.

MUST HAVE BEEN THAT DAMN SCRIPT YOU HAD ME READ-- GAVE ME NIGHTMARES.

I CAN'T REMEMBER WHAT IT WAS-- BUT I'M *ALL RIGHT* NOW.

IT WAS ONLY A DREAM...

...E NEXT ...ME BIG ...AMA ...OMES ...R ME...

...I FIGURE-- I'M SURE-- I'LL BE READY!

OF COURSE, SHE HAS OTHER IDEAS.

I'M NO MATCH FOR HER IN TERMS OF RAW STRENGTH.

I FIGURE TO MAKE UP THE DIFFERENCE WITH SPEED.

AND WHEN THAT DOESN'T WORK...

...TRY ...EAKY.

BEFORE I HIT THE FLOOR, THE CHAMELEON FIELD MAKES ME FUNCTIONALLY INVISIBLE.

AT WHICH POINT...

...I GET THE HELL OUT OF HER WAY!

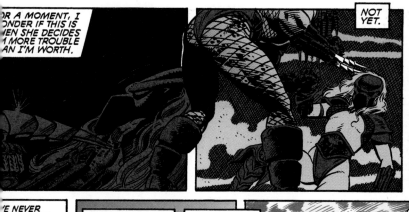

OR A MOMENT, I ONDER IF THIS IS EN SHE DECIDES M MORE TROUBLE AN I'M WORTH.

NOT YET.

I MUST BE GETTING BETTER.

'E NEVER T SO TIRED-- SO SORE.

DIDN'T ANY CHES, UNTIL END.

Y FIRST MISTAKE OULD HAVE EN MY LAST.

SHE'S TRAINING ME AS SHE WOULD ONE OF HER OWN.

I'M NOT YET HER EQUAL...

... BUT THAT DAY'S COMING.

WHO'D'VE THOUGHT A TROPHY HAD IT IN HER?

THEN, SUDDENLY, IT ISN'T A GAME ANYMORE.

NO!

MATER CHRISTI-- NO!

NOT SIMPLY AN ALIEN.

T A EN!

AS QUICK AS SHE IS SMART!

I KNOW I'M DEAD.

I PRAY IT WON'T HURT.

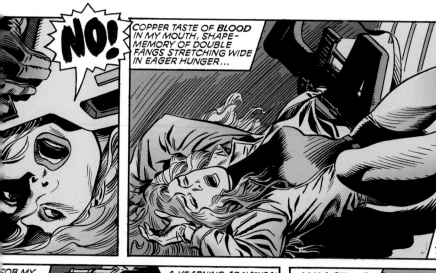

NO!

COPPER TASTE OF *BLOOD* IN MY MOUTH, SHAPE-MEMORY OF DOUBLE FANGS STRETCHING WIDE IN EAGER HUNGER...

...MY EYES SERVE NO FUNCTION I UNDERSTAND, THERE ARE SO MANY BETTER MEANS OF PERCEPTION, AS I GRAB REFLEXIVELY WITH LIMBS THAT DON'T EXIST TO STOP MY FALL...

SOB MY ART OUT.

A *GRIEF* I REFUSE TO COMPREHEND.

A *YEARNING* AS NATURAL AS I KNOW IT IS OBSCENE.

HAT IS PPENING O ME?!

WHAT IS HAPPENING TO ME?!

THE *ALIENS* ARE HUMANITY'S *ENEMY.*

AT'S THE *FUNDAMENTAL* ALITY OF OUR EXISTENCE.

HEY ARE THE EVIL MADE *FLESH.*

WHERE--?!

A SPACE STATION?!?

SPACE STATION SAMARA
DOCKING BAY 27

STARSHIP ELLEN RIPLEY

ASH PARNALL, COMMANDER

IT'S *ONLY* A *NIGHTMARE,* I TELL MYSELF.

BUT SO WERE MY *DREAMS* OF ASH PARNALL AND HER *PREDATOR.*

IT'S MORE THAN I CAN BEAR.

DAMN YOU BOTH! *DAMN YOU!*

I WON'T PLAY YOUR *PUPPET* ANYMORE!

ALL I WANT-- IS OUT.

I DON'T CONSIDER HOW I'LL GET THERE.

THE MOMENT I CYCLE THE FLIGHT-DECK HATCH, MY ATMOSPHERE'S OVERWHELMED BY THE PREDATOR'S.

ON MY WAY TOWARDS THE MAIN AIRLOCK...

...I COLLIDE FULL-TILT WITH THE PREDATOR'S COFFIN.

SHE DOESN'T NOTICE DON'T KNOW WHETHE SHE'S DEAD OR HEALIN

I DON'T CARE.

ASH... PARNALL...

SHUT UP!

I DON'T HEAR YOU! I'M *DONE* WITH YOU! WE'RE *THROUGH!*

I SHOULD HAVE SAVED MY BREATH.

IT ONLY MAKES M SICK.

I WAS MAD.

THAT'S THE ONLY EXPLANATION.

PERHAPS I STILL AM.

MERCIFUL GOD, HOW I WISH THIS WAS SOME *VIRTUAL* SCENARIO, ONE OF *TOY'S ADVENTURES.*

I'M SO TIRED.

YOUR DRINK, MA'AM.

I DON'T BELONG HERE.

WHAT COULD HAVE *POSSESSED* ME--?

I AM WHAT I *AM.* WHERE'S THE SHAME IN BEING A *TROPHY?* IT NEVER BOTHERED ME BEFORE NOW.

AND IT WON'T, EVER AGAIN.

ANOTH... PLEAS... THAT WA... GOOD...

I LABEL THIS A *BENCHMARK* MOMENT.

THE END OF *MISERY.*

WHEN NEXT I WAKE, I'LL BE HOME AND SAFE, AND ALL WILL BE *RIGHT* IN MY WORLD.

NAGEL! THE GODS HAVE *BLESSED* US BOTH TODAY, MY OLD COCK.

WHAT WOULD YO... SAY TO SALVA... ACCESS TO... *STARSHIP?*

I'M LISTENING.

IT'S IN BERTH 27, READY AND WAITING TO BE STRIPPED TO THE BARE METAL.

"THE OWNER'S IN MY LOUNGE, THREE SPECIALS ON THE ROAD TO BLISSFUL *OBLIVION.* SHE'S A *TROPHY,* NAGEL, CONFIRMED BY A FULL-SPECTRUM GENE-SCAN!"

"YOU'VE DONE *WELL,* KIRA MY DARLING. WE PUT HER ON THE *CIRCUIT*-- WITH THE PROPER PREP AND PRICE--

"--YOU AN' ME, WE'LL BE *SET FOR LIFE!*"

NEXT: *RUDE AWAKENINGS*

YOU GOTTA BE KIDDIN' ME, NAGEL--
--THIS IS WHAT ALL THE FUSS IS ABOUT?!
DON'T SCOFF, KIRA. CARYN DELACROIX IS A PRIME TROPHY...
...WHOSE HUBBY JUST HAPPENS TA BE ONE'A THE MOST POWERFUL CORPORATE EXECUTIVES IN KNOWN SPACE.
RUDE AWAKENINGS

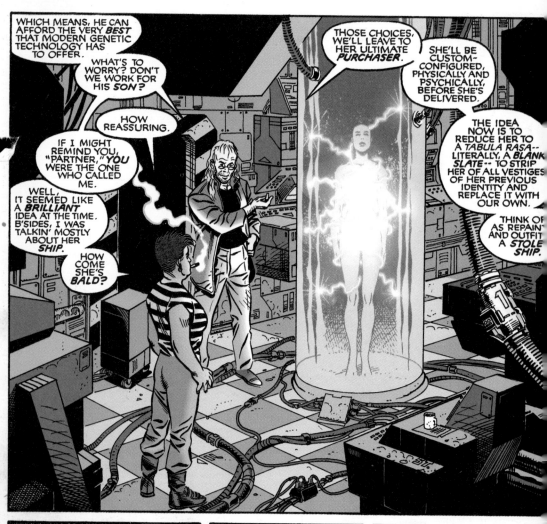

WHICH MEANS, HE CAN AFFORD THE VERY *BEST* THAT MODERN GENETIC TECHNOLOGY HAS TO OFFER.

WHAT'S TO WORRY? DON'T WE WORK FOR HIS *SON*?

HOW REASSURING.

IF I MIGHT REMIND YOU, "PARTNER," *YOU* WERE THE ONE WHO CALLED ME.

WELL, IT SEEMED LIKE A *BRILLIANT* IDEA AT THE TIME. B'SIDES, I WAS TALKIN' MOSTLY ABOUT HER *SHIP*.

HOW COME SHE'S *BALD*?

THOSE CHOICES, WE'LL LEAVE TO HER ULTIMATE *PURCHASER*.

SHE'LL BE CUSTOM-CONFIGURED, PHYSICALLY AND PSYCHICALLY, BEFORE SHE'S DELIVERED.

THE IDEA NOW IS TO REDUCE HER TO A *TABULA RASA*-- LITERALLY, A *BLANK SLATE*-- TO STRIP HER OF ALL VESTIGES OF HER PREVIOUS IDENTITY AND REPLACE IT WITH OUR OWN.

THINK OF IT AS REPAIR AND OUTFIT A *STOLE SHIP*.

LEAST'WAYS I KNOW WHAT I'M *SELLIN'* WITH A SHIP.

TRUST ME, KIRA. STAR-SHIPS, WE CAN GET ANYWHERE. A CREATURE LIKE THIS IS *UNIQUE*. WITH THE PRICE SHE'LL BRING, WE WON'T BE WORKIN' FOR THE *CIRCUIT* ANYMORE-- WE'LL *OWN* IT!

DON'T PASS FINAL JUDGMENT JUST YET, NOT UNTIL YOU'VE SEEN THE *IMPRINTING TEMPLATES* I'VE PREPARED. BY THE TIME WE'RE DONE *REPROGRAMMING* HER, SHE'LL BE *UNRECOGNIZABLE*-- EVEN TO *LUCIEN DELACROIX* HIMSELF!

EACH ELEMENT IS TAKEN TO ITS *ULTIMATE*, OFFERING THE WIDEST POSSIBLE RANGE OF TASTES AND PLEASURES. AND, BEST OF ALL, SHE'LL HAVE NO INHIBITIONS. THE CLIENT-- HER *OWNER*-- WILL BE THE MORAL CENTER OF HER REALITY. HER SOLE FUNCTION WILL BE TO PROVIDE ABSOLUTE SATISFACTION.

"IN EFFECT, ALL WE'RE DOING IS MODIFYING AND EXPANDING THE *CORE CONDITIONING* THAT ALREADY EXISTS WITHIN HER."

YOU CAN'T DO THAT!

NAGEL, SHE'S *AWARE!*

NO WAY, THAT'S NOT POSSIBLE!

NOT TO WORRY, NOT TO WORRY! I'VE GOT EVERYTHING UNDER CONTROL!

WHO *ARE* YOU? WHAT IS THIS PLACE?!

WHAT WE'RE SEEING IS THE PROJECTED ESSENCE OF THE WOMAN HER-SELF: THE SUM TOTAL OF HER MEMORY AND PERSONALITY, PROCESSED THROUGH OUR *ScanAlyzer* AND GIVEN PHYSICAL FORM.

WHY AM I HERE?! WHAT DO YOU *WANT* WITH ME?!

ANSWER, DAMN YOU!

YOU'RE A *SOMETHING* THAT'S ABOUT TO BE REDUCED TO *NOTHING.* DEAD IN ALL BUT NAME.

THE SYSTEM'S INITIALIZED. ALL I HAVE TO DO IS RUN THE PROGRAM AND YOU'RE *HISTORY,* MY DEAR. AND THEN, ALL THE OTHER TEMPLATES WILL RUSH IN TO FILL THE PSYCHIC VACUUM.

NO!

PLEASE! YOU *CAN'T!* YOU *MUSTN'T!*

LADY, IT'S *DONE!*

THE HELL YOU SAY!

I WON'T BE *ERASED!* I WON'T!

NAGEL, SHE'S NOT *DIS-CORPORATING!*

D'YOU THINK I'M *BLIND,* WOMAN?! I CAN *SEE* THAT!

THERE HAS TO BE A LOGICAL EXPLANATION. SOME FORM OF DEFENSIVE NETWORK PERHAPS--! NO MATTER THOUGH, IT'LL SOON BE *OVERWHELMED.*

STOP THIS, I BEG YOU! *PLEASE.*

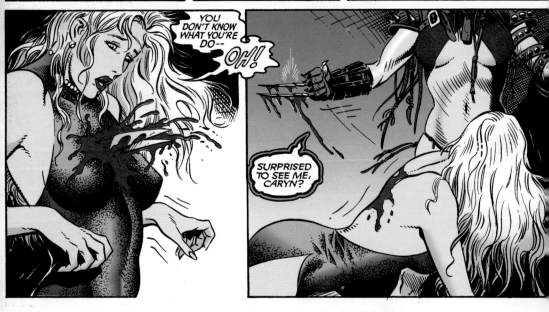

YOU DON'T KNOW WHAT YOU'RE DO-- *OH!*

SURPRISED TO SEE ME, CARYN?

BACK! EVERYBODY, *BACK!*

CLEAR THIS PLATFORM!

CEN-COM, THIS IS *GENNA*, BAY 27-- I WANT A *MEDEVAC CRASH TEAM*, ON SCENE, ON THE DOUBLE!

HOMER'S COUGHING BLOOD-- I THINK THERE'S MAJOR LUNG TRAUMA-- NO OTHER CASUALTIES.

AIRLOCK'S COVERED, PARTNER! YOUR BACK'S CLEAR!

CHILL, SADIQ. IT'S A HOSTILE ATMOSPHERE, NOTHING MORE.

IZZAT SO? YOU WANNA TELL ME THEN HOW A *STANDARD HUMAN* BIOFORM CAN BREATHE *METHANE?*

SOLE PASSENGER WAS A *TROPHY.* MAYBE SHE DOESN'T NEED TO BREATHE AT ALL.

BART, FLASH KIRA, COPY TO CEN-COM. I WANT A *COMBAT CADRE* SCRAMBLED, FOR *BACK-UP.*

SADIQ AND I'LL HANDLE THE RECONNAISSANCE.

YOU'RE *WELCOME* TO IT!

OKAY, HOTBOT, YOU READY TO PLAY *HERO?*

AND HERE I THOUGHT YOU ONLY VALUED ME FOR MY *GOOD LOOKS.*

TEMPTING THOUGHT-- IF YOU *HAD* ANY.

INITIATING FULL-SPECTRUM SCAN.

NEGATIVE MOVEMENT, NEGATIVE LIFESIGNS, MINIMAL POWER EMANATIONS.

WHAT'D I TELL YOU? A *DERELICT.* THE TROPHY PROBABLY CAME OUT OF A *FREEZER,* AN STRAIGHT FOR THE *EXIT.*

IF YOU SAY SO.

THAT BEIN' THE CASE, SWEET, MIND EXPLAININ' *THIS?*

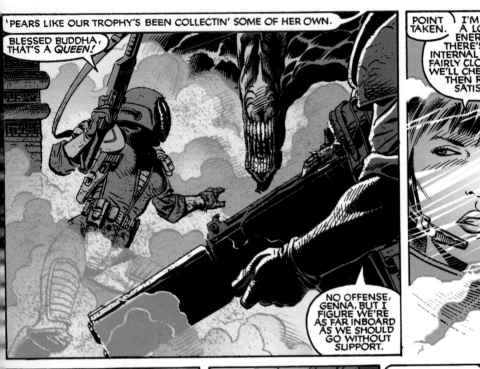

'PEARS LIKE OUR TROPHY'S BEEN COLLECTIN' SOME OF HER OWN.

BLESSED BUDDHA, THAT'S A *QUEEN!*

NO OFFENSE, GENNA, BUT I FIGURE WE'RE AS FAR INBOARD AS WE SHOULD GO WITHOUT SUPPORT.

POINT TAKEN. I'M SCOPING A LOCALIZED ENERGY NEXUS. THERE'S A LIVE INTERNAL SYSTEM, FAIRLY CLOSE BY. WE'LL CHECK IT OUT, THEN RABBIT. SATISFIED?

YOU GOT THE RANK-- GUESS THAT MEANS YOU GOT THE *BRAINS.*

UP YOURS.

IT'S A *LIFEPOD!* FLASH KIRA, SADIQ, I THINK WE'VE GOT ANOTHER *LIVE* ONE!

OUT- STANDING. ANOTHER "LIVE ONE" *WHAT?*

HALF A SEC, I'LL LET YOU KNOW.

UP... YOURS!

KLUDD!

DAMN YOU *DAMN YOU* **DAMN YOU!**

THAT WAS MY *PARTNER!*

GENNA, *DISENGAGE!* YOU'RE *BLOCKING* MY *SHOT!*

DAMN YOU...

...THAT WAS *MY PARTNER!*

BLAM

SADIQ!

K-RAK

NO *GUN?*

BETTER HIS WAY!

I LIKE MY VENGEANCE *PERSONAL!*

BY THE WAY...

...WHAT'S ALL THIS *GREEN GOOP*--

--BLOOD?

YOU *HURTING*, UGLY?

NO PROBLEM. I GOT JUST THE *CURE!*

MAYDAY *MAYDAY*
MAYDAY--
CADRE BRAVO--
WE'RE BEIN'
MASSACRED--

--OMI*GOD*,
IT'S COMIN'
FOR *ME!*

BRAWRR

CADRE BRAVO...
BEEN
MASSACRED...

...DAMN
QUICK, TOO...

HAHAHAHAHA HA HA HA HA
HA

MOTHERLESS

FATHERLESS

BASTARD

WHATEVER
HELL YOU CAME
FROM...

...WHATEVER
BROUGHT YOU
HERE--

AN ALIEN!

AN ALIEN ON THE STATION. CEN-COM'S GOTTA BE TOLD. MERCIFUL ALLÁH, IF THERE'S ONE--!

AND YOU!

YOU TRIED TO KILL ME BEFORE, BUT NOW YOU SAVE MY LIFE! WHAT THE HELL GOES ON HERE? WHAT KIND OF CREATURE ARE YOU?!

RRRAKT!

--I JUST NAILED THEIR QUEEN!

EVERYTHING-- STOPPED?!

SIMULATION'S PROGRAMMED TO *FREEZE* WHENEVER EITHER SIDE "WINS."

SO, SINCE *MARIA* FRIED THE *BIG BITCH BUG*, THAT MUST BE *US!*

WAY TO *GO!*

HIGH FIVES, CREW, FOR THE *TEAM SUPREME!* LEMME *HAVE* 'EM!

OR NOT. WHATEVER.

NICE PIECE OF WORK, THAT *ENERGY WEAPON* OF YOURS, MARIA.

I'M CERTAINLY IMPRESSED.

WHAT'S ITS PROVENANCE?

MADAME DELACROIX'S CRITTER.

WE ONLY HA THE OPPORTUN FOR SOME PRELI NARY TESTS BEFO WE LEFT...

...BUT ITS DEFAULT-TRACKING AND TARGETING SYSTEMS APPEAR TO BE KEYED TO *BUGS.*

WHEREVER THAT *PREDATOR* CAME FROM, IT'S FOUGHT *ALIENS* BEFORE.

YOU SHOUL TURN IT OV TO *TOY.*

WHAT'RE YOU *TELLING* ME, GENNA?!

THAT YOUR CADRE OF *SUPPOSEDLY* TRAINED, *SUPPOSEDLY* EXPERIENCED, *SUPPOSEDLY* COMPETENT TROOPERS...

...COULDN'T HANDLE A LONE, UNARMED EXOTIC?

AND A *WOUNDED* ONE AT THAT?!

WHAT THE HELL HAVE I BEEN PAYING YOU FOR ALL THESE YEARS?

LOOK AT ME, NAGEL! YOU THINK THIS IS *MAKE-UP?!*

THIS CREATURE'S LIKE *NOTHING* I'VE EVER FOUGHT.

I'D RATE AS *DANGER* AS A BU—

I DON'T WANT TO HEAR IT!

WHAT COMES NEXT, SWEETHEART-- YOU WANT ME TO BRING IN THE *COLONIAL MARINES?!*

ACTUALLY, YES!

WON'T *THAT* PLEASE OUR *CORPORATE* EMPLOYERS!

MAY I REMIND YOU, WOMAN, THAT THIS IS AN *ILLEGAL* OPERATION. YOU'RE HERE SO WE WON'T *NEED* OUTSIDE ASSISTANCE.

YOU'VE BEEN *WELL PAID* FOR YOUR EXPERTISE, GENNA.

NOW *EARN* IT.

NO MOR QUESTIO NO MOR EXCUSE

I WA THE EX FOUN I WAN *KILL*

Also available from Boxtree

DISSECTING ALIENS: TERROR IN SPACE

IN SPACE NO ONE CAN HEAR YOU SCREAM . . . .

Remember the horror of Jaws? Transport it to the far reaches of outer-space, and you have entered the terrifying world of *Alien*.

DISSECTING ALIENS: TERROR IN SPACE is a comprehensive behind-the-scenes look at the phenomenal film series, examining in minute detail the making of *ALIEN, ALIENS* and *ALIEN 3*.

Beyond the trilogy, author John L. Flynn discloses tantalizing details regarding earlier drafts of the films and explores unproduced adventures – including three completely different versions of *ALIEN 3* and *ALIEN VS PREDATOR* – and previews the currently-in-development *ALIEN 4*. In addition to the celluloid *ALIEN* there is a whole range of comic books and novels based on the scenario that are indexed and studied here. DISSECTING ALIENS even provides a guide to the various items of *ALIEN* memorabilia that have become available over the years.

RELIVE THE HORROR OF *ALIEN!*

Publication Date: 31 March 1995
Author: John L. Flynn
Price: £9.99 pb
ISBN: 0 7522 0863 2

Coming soon from Boxtree

ALIENS COLONIAL MARINES
TECHNICAL MANUAL

"CHECK IT OUT! We've got tactical smart missiles, phased plasma cannon, pulse rifles, RPGs; we've got nukes, we've got knives, sharp sticks . . . !"

The United States Colonial Marines. Ultimate troubleshooters equipped with state-of-the-art firepower, capable of power projection across the vast expanse of deep space. They can sharpshoot a man at a thousand metres or obliterate an entire world from the safety of orbit. They reckon they are unbeatable.

But on a dirtball colony planet known only as LV-426 the unthinkable happened.

The Marines lost.

The ALIENS COLONIAL MARINES TECHNICAL MANUAL is your official guide to the equipment and organisation of the United States Colonial Marine Corps. Packed with never-before-published diagrams, technical schematics and plans, the manual takes a look at the guns, vehicles and ships of the USCMC and the men and women who use them.

A must for all ALIENS fans, this book examines the technology of the film's futuristic nightmare in every detail, and tries to discover exactly what went wrong on LV-426.

Publication Date: 31 March 1995
Author: Lee Brimmicombe-Wood
Price: £13.99 pb
ISBN: 0 7522 0844 6

GRAPHIC NOVELS AVAILABLE FROM BOXTREE

☐ 1-85283-395-5	X-Men: Wolverine	£6.99pb
☐ 1-85283-390-4	X-Men: Brood Trouble In The Big Easy	£5.25pb
☐ 0-75220-892-6	X-Men Adventures	£9.99pb
☐ 0-75220-871-3	X-Men: God loves, Man kills	£5.99pb
☐ 0-75220-803-9	X-Men: Sabretooth	£6.99pb
☐ 0-75220-691-5	Ghostrider/Wolverine/Punisher – Hearts of Darkness/Dark Design	£7.99pb
☐ 0-75220-987-6	Star Wars – Dark Empire	£9.99pb
☐ 0-75220-913-2	Star Wars Classic	£7.99pb
☐ 0-75220-817-9	Star Wars – Tales of the Jedi and Freedom Nadd Uprising	£10.99pb
☐ 0-75220-616-8	Star Wars – Dark Lords of Sith 1	£8.99pb
☐ 0-75220-804-7	Star Wars – Droids	£8.99pb
☐ 0-75220-822-5	Star Wars – Dark Empire 2	£9.99pb
☐ 0-75220-928-0	Star Trek: Deep Space Nine	£7.99pb
☐ 0-75220-933-7	Star Trek: Deep Space Nine – Emancipation and Beyond	£7.99pb
☐ 0-75220-898-5	Star Trek: Deep Space Nine – Hearts and Minds	£7.99pb
☐ 0-75220-851-9	Ranma book 1	£5.99pb
☐ 0-75220-861-6	Ranma book 2	£5.99pb
☐ 0-75220-881-0	Mask (film tie-in)	£6.99pb
☐ 0-75220-856-X	Shadow (film tie-in)	£6.99pb
☐ 0-75220-962-0	Necroscope	£7.99pb
☐ 0-75220-977-9	RoboCop: Prime Suspect	£7.99pb
☐ 0-75220-876-4	Spider-Man: the return of the Sinister Six	£9.99pb
☐ 0-75220-897-7	Daredevil – man without fear	£9.99pb
☐ 0-75220-645-1	Marvels	£10.99pb
☐ 0-75220-808-X	Spider-Man: revenge of the sinister 6	£7.99pb
☐ 0-75220-878-0	Aliens v Predator – deadliest of the Species 1	£9.99pb
☐ 0-75220-813-6	Street Fighter II – book 1	£6.99pb
☐ 0-75220-818-7	Street Fighter II – book 2	£6.99pb

All these books are available at your local bookshop or newsagent or can be ordered direct from the publisher. Just tick the titles you want and fill in the form below.

Prices and availability are subject to change without notice.

Boxtree Cash Sales, P.O. Box 11, Falmouth, Cornwall TR10 9EN

Please send a cheque or postal order for the value of the book and add the following for postage and packing:

U.K. including B.F.P.O. – £1.00 for one book plus 50p for the second book, and 30p for each additional book ordered up to a £3.00 maximum.

OVERSEAS INCLUDING EIRE – £2.00 for the first book plus £1.00 for the second book, and 50p for each additional book ordered.

OR please debit this amount from my Access/Visa Card (delete as appropriate).

Card Number ☐☐☐☐☐☐☐☐☐☐☐☐☐☐☐☐

Amount £ ....

Expiry Date ....

Signed ....

Name ....

Address ....